Write Your Heart Out:
Advice From the Moon Winx Motel

Write Your Heart Out:
Advice From the Moon Winx Motel

A NOVEL

G E O F F   S C H M I D T

 smallmouth press

Smallmouth Press
P. O. Box 661
New York, NY 10185-0661
www.smallmouthpress.com

"Chapter Two: Inspiration" first appeared in *The Distillery*

FIRST EDITION

1 2 3 4 5 6 7 8 9 . 07 06 05 04 03 02 01 00

Library of Congress Cataloging-in-Publication Data
Schmidt, Geoff
Write your heart out: advice from the moon winx motel /
Geoff Schmidt. — 1st Ed.

ISBN 1-58848-010-0

Book Design by Christopher Chambers

Printed in the United States of America

CONTENTS

Foreword 1

PART THREE

Revise

For my wife, Nicola, who gives my life meaning.

The first time I saw Gus Jones, he walked into our seminar room, put his briefcase down flat at the head of the table, opened it, pulled out a gun, and pointed it at my head. (I had in those days an unfortunate eagerness to impress, and had chosen the seat to the left of what I knew would be Professor Jones's.) "This semester," he said, looking not at me but at each member of our workshop, "you will by God write as if it mattered." Then he pulled the trigger. (Later, this story would somehow get attached to Barry Hannah, who would always deny it. Gus was never eager to claim credit, and would now say it never happened, would in fact say he'd heard it *was* Barry Hannah who pulled a gun on his class, but I was there. I looked down the barrel of that gun. I know.)

The gun wasn't loaded, of course.

So this was how I met my mentor, the man who would make me the writer I am today, and let me tell you that I never forgot the lesson of that day, though I would be hard-pressed to articulate it. Let me instead say that fiction matters. And this book, unlike most other books you will read about writing fiction, matters.

This book is a cocked gun pointed at your head. It's Gus's finger on the trigger, from beyond the grave.

We don't know quite when he died, but we know where: at a motel desk, working on this book. It seems ghoulish to tell you what page was still there flickering on his computer screen, behind which word his cursor was blinking when the massive coronary struck and killed him dead. If you read closely, you might be able to hazard a good guess. When his ex-wife Penelope found him, he'd been dead for several days. His head was thrown back, his arms spread wide, his eyes half shut, as if closing them on Heaven. I think he would be pleased for you to take this image of him with you as you begin to read.

Fiction matters.

Gus had been working on this book off and on for many, many years. It was one of his most cherished projects, and one he tinkered with obsessively.

In some small way, I like to think I had a part in the birth of this book. I was still his student, and could only have dreamed of the success that would later come my way. We were sitting on his porch on a Sunday morning, sipping screwdrivers out of Mason jars with our feet up on the porch rail. Gus was sitting next to me. He was still married then, and happy, I think. It was April, hot but not yet steamy (this was in Alabama), the grass newly mown and enthusiastically green. The porch was shaded, a breeze stirring the wind chimes he loved. Penelope, his wife, was still asleep inside.

"I wish I could write like this day feels," I said. I was then twenty-three, and said many things aloud that I would not say now.

"Where is the cool, lucid prose of yesteryear?" he said, more drunk than mocking.

Then Penelope came out, blinking, in bare feet and her summer-weight nightgown (pale blue), and leaned over and kissed him, and I did not stare at her cleavage but out at the green yard and the wet clumps of grass, and Penelope made a face when she tasted the screwdriver on his mouth, and straightened. She made a face at me then, a scrunched-nose mock-grimace, and went inside. Gus forgot all about our conversation, and ambled in after her. How he loved Penelope! To tell you the truth, I'm surprised he lived as many years as he did after their marriage fell apart. I sat on the porch until I heard them making love inside, and then I stood and ambled off myself.

I thought he'd forgotten our conversation. A few weeks later, after workshop, he slid a manila folder across the table to me. Inside were ten pages called "How to Write Like A Morning Is"—what is now Chapter Thirteen of this book.

She still loved him.

Even after things went so wrong, after she left him, even up to the very end, she loved him. How else to explain her visit to his motel room? How else to explain what she

wanted when she found his body? She has never told anyone what brought her to the Moon Winx Motel that day.

What else could it be but love?

She called me from the phone at the front desk. She said
later that she could not speak in front of his body. She
sounded calm on the phone. It was only later that she broke
down. Of course she loved him.

I came over right away. I had just jetted in from New
York where I had received the National Book Award. I was
beyond exhaustion. The day lives surreally in my
memory—in just twelve hours I'd won the National Book
Award and lost my mentor—a blur of applause and ambu-
lances, supersonic jets and gurneys, the tuxedoed elite
and derelict onlookers, his corpse, oh his corpse, and the
rattle of the air conditioner, and the hum of his computer
monitor, and the white pages of draft after draft of the
manuscript of this book, scattered over the desk and the
sink and the bed and the aggressively bland rug. Gus had
no literary executor, and his agent and all of his editors had
long ago dropped him, but both Penelope and I knew that
we would do everything we could to see this last work,
especially, published. Jet-lagged, bleary with words, I held
her in that ugly room while she wept. We both vowed, then
and later, to make sure that this book was given to the
world.

Because no matter what, Gus was a teacher. No matter
what he did to his own life, or the lives of those close to
him, he never lost his passion for teaching. No matter how
his own career faltered, he could always inspire his students

to greatness. No one will ever get another chance to experience his genius as a teacher, but this book captures a slice of it. It does his memory justice.

This book matters.

I decided to publish it as is, incomplete, rough spots and all. Gus himself was full of rough spots. I think he might have liked for the world to know this about him, when so often they saw only the polished mirror of his prose. And Gus himself was incomplete, a work-in-progress, as everyone who knew him surely recognized.

For a man who claimed always to cherish honesty, I can think of no greater tribute than to publish a rough and incomplete book.

I just wish he were alive to see it.

—Andrew Shay

PART ONE

Think

Annihilating all that's made
To a green thought in a green shade.
                          — Andrew Marvell, "The Garden"

CHAPTER ONE:
WRITING PAST
THE MILLENNIUM

Dear readers, gentle readers, good souls and bad, all those here assembled, I can't tell you how happy I am that you're reading this book. So, first, welcome. And by way of welcome, let me make a few observations.

Most of the "how-to" books you've read before this one have been worthless. You and I both know this is true. If they had done their job, you would be happily published, and every aspect of your life would be rich and rewarding— public admiration, personal contentment, spiritual enlightenment, terrific sex. And I'm sure you wouldn't be reading this book. Yet here you are. Is that your fault? No! The blame for that lies squarely with those other "how-to" book writers, not you. Those writers failed you because not one of them was honest.

There are at least three reasons for this. First, many "self-help" books are written by—why not be honest about it?—hacks. When is the last time you saw John Irving or Joyce

Carol Oates or John Updike or Alice Walker or Andrew Shay writing books about mastering dialogue or devising plots or creating realistic characters? Such literary lights are generally far too busy being successful—until now. If you picked this book up, I suspect it's in part because you've seen my name on the bestseller lists *and* favorably mentioned on the front page of *The New York Times Book Review* (well, my first book, anyway). And I care—I have had my successes, dear gentle readers, yet I still care about you. Never forget this when you become successful. I have had students who have gone on to great success who have forgotten who was there with them at the start—they have forgotten how to care.

The ex-students I have come to respect are the ones who continue to acknowledge in some public forum all of the influences that have worked on their young souls. Andrew Shay, for example, has always mentioned me and other teachers who had a formative effect on him. Andrew, in fact, has kept in close touch with me, sending cards, stopping in for visits, sending care packages to my wife (when we were together), remembering the girls' birthdays. When he was my student, he was always over at the house, and in many ways it feels like he's never left, that he's still a part of our lives. Try to be like that for the people who cared about you.

I care.

Second, most of the people who write these books are too polite, or too modest. They don't tell you the truth because they are trying not to offend you. They have this picture in their head of you, dear wonderful reader, as someone who is untalented, or prudish, or hopelessly Nebraskan, pathetically amateurish—they don't want to offend your dilettante sensibility. Let me be the first to call bullshit on that. I am a profane man, yes, maybe even offensive in some small or large ways, but I am a smart offensive man, and one who respects you. Let me say it again: I respect you (these are, in fact, nearly the first words I said to my wife, and in many ways, writing a book is like falling in love and getting married, though of course my marriage ended, but that's not really germane to my general point). It bears repeating: I respect you. I respect you, yes, and I will not pigeonhole you, I will not assume that plain talk and salty language and honesty will offend you. I'll tell it like it is, and in my own words.

If you *are* hopelessly Nebraskan, however, well, forewarned, and all that. I have had students drop my courses in the past, and while they would have said that some aspect of my teaching style was the reason for that, the true reason is that they were not serious enough about themselves or their art to listen to the truth, unvarnished.

I promise I will always give you truth. I promise I will always withhold the varnish.

Third, and truly awful, most professional writers don't want competition. It's shocking, but most "how-to" books are "how-NOT-to" books. And deliberately so! Incredible, isn't it? If you're skimming these opening pages in your local Waldenbooks, look at the rest of the names on the shelf next to this book. Go ahead, look.

All of those men and women want you to fail.

I want you to succeed. I want you to be a writer, a professional, publishing, artistically brilliant writer, and I will teach you how—yes, gentle ones, good writing CAN be taught, and it WILL be taught. TALENT CAN BE TAUGHT! Never forget that.

Here at the edge of the millennium, though, we want more than talent. We want to write well *and* be wildly successful. At the very least, we want to be published. Here at the edge of another thousand years, we want words that will last, words that will survive, words that will be tattooed in blue on the backs of our children's children, words that will be taken into the bunkers.

So what will that bunker-fiction look like?

In the fiction of the future, plot will be much more important than it is now. Plot will dominate a narrative like a Sumo wrestler. Also, we're surrounded by so many fast bright shiny moving objects—fiction must compete not just with MTV but with the three-dimensional virtual reality versions of MTV that surely lurk just around the corner.

To compete, THINGS MUST HAPPEN!

In the fiction of the future, prose style will get simpler and simpler. Down in the bunker, people will have a lot to worry about—they won't want to work too hard figuring out sentences. Because of this, you will find that chapters and novels will get shorter, too. Always try to keep an image of your audience member in mind, lugging around a laptop or a portable tattoo kit—write for those poor readers down in the bunkers of the future.

In fact, in the future, fiction writers will either have to take a few art courses or make friends with some good graphic artists—how their fiction looks on the page will be important like never before! Just ask Nicholson Baker why he's taking that pottery class, or Annie Proulx what she's doing with that brush in her hand. The fiction of the future will not just have to do with words, my devoted reader!

In fact, in the future we will not be novelists or short story writers; we will be fictioneers, blazing new ground, breeding new hybrids, fracturing new syntaxes. Or, as my poker buddies William Kennedy, Ishmael Reed, Tom Chiarella, and Joy Williams might suggest (in unison), "Shut up and deal." And in the future, every game will be a wild card game!

Most of all, though, remember that the best words are the words that help you or others see clearly what was not clear before. And to feel love. When I think of words, a great love fills me, a cosmic force-field of love. And when I think of the times (well, the one time) in my life when I was truly in love, what I think of are the words we shared, the language that bound us. Be in love with your words, darling readers. Caress them. Tell them how special they are. Do not, oh do not, do not be tempted to verbicide.

I will tell you everything I know. Everything that has ever worked for me. Every last secret of my writer's soul. I will give you good advice and examples from real life and exercises to develop your artistic muscles. I will share with you everything I know, and when I am done, some or all of those secrets will nuzzle their way into the folds of your soul, take root, and blossom, so that your soul will sprout green seedlings of talent that will grow and grow over your soul like ivy. When you have finished this book, your soul will be verdant and leafy with talent (see Chapter XX: "Extending A Metaphor") just like the greenest writers I know.

You deserve to be as green as they are. Welcome, then, to this greenhouse of the writer's soul. Welcome, and read on. Plant food and compost await you.

CHAPTER TWO:
INSPIRATION

Where do the best books come from?

Beginning a book is like falling in love. They sneak up on you, the best books do. They are like the woman you've known for years as a friend, the woman who has brown shiny hair and beautiful brown eyes, who is funny and sexy in ways you've never known until suddenly, somehow, some fall night, you see her with fresh eyes, the scales lifted, holy cow, holy cow, why didn't I ever see *that* before?! That's what it's like with books, too, at first. My first collection of short stories came together like a revelation, that same rush of surprise and recognition, energy and curiosity, abandon and control. And it can be so sudden, so suggestive of divine intervention that as many people use Cupid to describe that first romantic tumble, so too do many writers talk about being visited by the Muse.

I was, then, too young, too impossibly full of myself, to realize that my Muse was real, not metaphoric. Oh, what a snot I was! I can't apologize enough for that. In 1983, I was twenty-five, in my first year of graduate school, when my story "The Station Wagon" was pulled by Will Blythe from the slush pile at *Esquire*. Incredible luck, but of course I was too callow to acknowledge that. And when that story became the centerpiece of their issue on "Hot Young Writers Under Twenty-Six," did I appreciate how fortunate I was? And when they ran my picture on the cover with the headline "Are You Jonesin'?" could I know how that catch phrase would stick? I was Jonesin'. I was Jonesin' right through my MFA program, right into my first tenure-track teaching job, right into the Absolut ads and the book contracts. Could I know how many buckets full of drool would be filled by agents the world over? No, I was Jonesin'. Was I humble when my first collection, *People in Cars*, was published in 1985? Did I take it in stride when I appeared on Letterman, when at conferences they put me on panels with Tama Janowitz and Bret Easton Ellis and Jay McInerny? Oh, hell no, I was Jonesin' in my Ray Bans, slurping my designer vodka and chain-smoking my Dunhills and radiating attitude. "Are…you… *Jonesin'*!?" I would say before every reading, and (oh shame) to the groupies I slept with—I was twenty-four/five/six and I had groupies! I had everything. (I had everything but that second book, a lesson for another chapter (note to self: write that chapter)).

Of course my Muse was there the whole time, agonized. I just couldn't be bothered to see her. I was too in love with the idea that all that success equaled all that talent that must surely be mine, all mine. Need I add the mad-scientist-esque "mwah-ha-ha-ha-ha" that would always follow that phrase? Eager hand-rubbing optional, as always.

Of course I hit bottom by 1989 or 1990, but this book is not about me, and this chapter is all about Muses. Writers who tell you they don't believe in Muses never really LOOKED, (they may SEE, but they do not LOOK) and those poor almost-writers will never write their way past the millennium, as we will, dear readers. I have much to atone for. Come on board the Millennium Bus with me! Warp speed ahead! Pack your lunches and fill your flasks and save a seat for your Muses!

Seven or eight years ago, when I finally LOOKED, I saw that my Muse dressed in peach-dyed silk and had paper-thin wings and looked just like (my now-ex-wife) Penelope, her brown hair shining. Each bright morning my Muse would hover by the side of the bed and awaken me with her ethereal humming. Groggy, I would take her hand and she would lead me to my study, and sit me down, and turn on my computer. While it booted up she went and poured me a cup of coffee, and brought it to me, and then curled up on top of the monitor and purred rhythmically, and the sound of her purring and my fingers on the keyboard was like the sweet rumble of thunder and the rain that washed over us every afternoon, which is when I would look up from my computer and stretch, and stand, and bow to my Muse, and wander off to make love to Penelope.

When Penelope left much later with the kids, my Muse went into the Muse Relocation Program. I never heard from her again. Maybe you've seen her? For all I know, she'll be purring on your monitor as soon as you put this book down and begin your own wonderful projects, darling readers.

My replacement muse is named Muse X. She wears thick mascara and changes her hair color weekly. She has ninety-seven piercings, thirty-one tattoos, and a Ph.D. in French Literature, but refuses to teach me the language. She prefers leather and denim, likes fishnet stockings. From her white neck on separate chains dangle hundreds of different religious icons. She reads Aeschylus and Euripides and Aristophanes, even the lost works, just to taunt me. She listens to Liz Phair and Johnny Cash and the Replacements and Mozart and the Lower Chakras and Public Enemy on a half-melted Walkman. She sliced off her wings. She drives a Cherry Red Corvette. She speaks English with a Greek accent. She refuses to do any paperwork, visits irregularly, and often comes to me reeling drunk.

You can pick your friends, but you can't choose your Muse. If this one leaves me, though, I shudder to think what might come next.

Anyway, on to some practical advice:

Things To Do With Your Muse

I TAKE YOUR MUSE BOWLING

This is especially effective if your Muse is uptight or pretentious. A few pitchers, some ill-fitting bowling shoes, and a half dozen gutter balls later, your Muse will have lightened up considerably. At the end of the evening, if one or both of you is trying to sneak out still wearing your bowling shoes, you know your writing will be blessed. A few words of warning: Always let your Muse win, always buy the drinks, and don't get jealous if that guy (or woman) the next lane over with the wrist guard and the plastic hair and the too-tight jeans who just bowled 190 starts to hit on your Muse. Be secure in your own skills and know that at the end of the night the Muse will most probably come home with you, if you have been attentive, considerate, kind, mature, loving, all those good things. Muses don't leave, but they can be driven away. Take it from someone who's been there before.

2 TAKE YOUR MUSE TO THE ZOO

Who doesn't like to see the monkeys swing, the peacocks strut, the tigers roar, the bears growl and lumber? Who doesn't shake their heads at the irony of the pigeons that chase peanuts while the jeweled birds peck at the glass of their cages? Who doesn't imagine what it might be like to jump the fence, traverse the moat, not to touch the animals or chase them, but just to be there, on the other side? Who among us has not wanted to hide in the bathroom until the zoo was closed, then slip out into the shadows, wander the dark paths? The zoo experience will help you and your Muse bond. You will feel closer to each other, secure in the fact that you are not animals, and that you do not live in cages.

3 TAKE YOUR MUSE BAR-HOPPING

Like people, some Muses can hold their liquor and some can't. Either way, one of you will drink the other under the table, and then the rules of your relationship will be firmly established. There's nothing like puking your brains out while your Muse holds a cold washcloth to your forehead to let you know who's in control. Similarly, once you, slightly less drunk, drive your Muse, mumbling and drooling, home, and put him or her to bed on his or her stomach, and slump in a chair by that bed, afraid he or she will choke on his or her own vomit, sleeping fitfully through the rest of the night, then you will be able to summon your Muse with more assurance.

4 TAKE YOUR MUSE TO THE AIRPORT

Airports are sort of like zoos for humans. You get to see so many different kinds of people. Buy some peanuts and popcorn and sit down at a gate. Go ahead and critique the people as they walk by—only your Muse will hear you! One day, my Muse and I saw a pale woman with blond hair crying soundlessly as she sat in the gate area. We stared at her openly. She had an interesting weeping technique— she opened her mouth and it trembled and tears and snot slid down her face but she did not otherwise move or make a sound. We were moved to pity, my Muse and I, and at last got up and offered her a facial tissue, at which point she flinched, and bit my hand. We left before she could call security, which we somehow felt sure was the next thing she would do. And while that moment never actually made it into a story, my Muse used it as a moment of painful inspiration.

5 TAKE YOUR MUSE TO THE PLAYGROUND

I would never have thought of this before Chloe and Miranda were born. Even in the darker days near the end, of which I can not bear really to speak, and don't even mean to mention now (note to self: revise, revise, revise), I still took the girls to the park to play on the swingsets and the teeter-totters and the climbing thingies. Some writers I know have even built their own elaborate playgrounds in their own elaborate back yards—Rita Ciresi and Steve Sherrill and Alice McDermott all have state-of-the-art merry-go-rounds and curvy slides available to them twenty-four/seven.

Muses love to be around children, even frightening post-punk indifferent Muses.

6 TAKE YOUR MUSE TO THE SHEMP FESTIVAL

Oh, Shemp, unsung genius of the Three Stooges! If you can't ignite the inspirational fires in a Muse, I don't know who can. When I still taught at the University of Alabama, my colleagues Laura Hendrie and Kevin Stein and Amy Newman all turned me on to the Shemp Festival. Held in Donaldsonville, Louisiana, it's an annual bacchanalia/appreciation revolving around Shemp Howard—twenty-four-hour film festival, live music, town-wide pie fights, the crowning of the Pie Queen, and the best etouffée I've ever tasted. I enjoyed it so much Penelope and I timed our wedding so we could spend our honeymoon at the Shemp Festival (Festival in-fighting, though, and a contentious faction that believed a—shudder—Curly Joe Festival would be more commercial, left us with a sour taste in our mouths and we went to someplace lushly tropical instead).

Dear reader, now that I think about it, I don't even know if they still hold the Shemp Festival. That all happened a very long time ago.

Never mind.

7 TAKE YOUR MUSE TO THE RODEO

Now, I've never been to a rodeo, and have never taken my Muse to one, but my Muse insists she'd like to see one. "Cowboys with washboard stomachs, wild horses, bulls— what's not to like?" says my Muse, eyeing my slight beer belly ("like a pregnant snake," she says in an almost-aside. She's barking up the wrong tree—since Penelope left and took the house and kids with her, my humiliation level knows no limit). I admit I'd like to see a rodeo for the sheer spectacle of it. I shrug. In the words of what's-his-name, there will be all manner of time. Maybe someday.

"Soon," she says sadly, soberly. "It has to be soon."

Places Not to Take Your Muse

I DO NOT TAKE YOUR MUSE TO THE LIBRARY, ART GALLERY, RECITAL HALL, OR EVEN TO THE LOCAL CINEPLEX.

He or she might get ideas—I mean, how well is your stuff going to stack up? Maybe your Muse is tired of your hours, or bored with your malarkey—maybe your Muse is angling for a better gig. Trust is a good thing in any Muse-writer relationship, but why put ideas in his or her head? Keep your Muse away from Art (though you yourself can sneak out and take in a show or a gallery opening, if you can distract your Muse long enough. Still, she might smell the Art on you, and then get suspicious, and start to sabotage your efforts, and then where will you be? Play it safe, and avoid High Culture.) Okay, you're probably safe at the local Mega-Movie-32-Plex. Probably.

2 DO NOT TAKE YOUR MUSE TO BED

You may be tempted. You'll both be working late, and the creative nature of your work together can be intoxicating. You'll brush fingers, perhaps, while reaching for the type-writer, or sit too carelessly close, and you'll feel that frisson, that spark. Never confuse this with sexual energy, though. If you redirect that energy you redefine your relationship, you change it, and your Muse will now be your lover, and will now rightly expect you to spend your time in bed attending to his or her every need, not at the keyboard. And while he or she may be the most incredibly skilled lover you've ever encountered—I mean, you'd expect that, right?—trust me, oh, trust me, dear good gentle readers, when I tell you that all relationships are ephemeral. No lover stays, no love lasts. You can love your Muse, but do not make love to him, her, or it.

3 DO NOT TAKE YOUR MUSE TO HELL

Muses, whatever their appearances, are delicate, ephemeral beings. Trips to Hell, metaphoric or literal, will muss their hair and singe their wings, and most likely piss them off badly assuming they survive the trip. If you happen to find yourself in Hell, wait until you're out before you summon your Muse. Or, to put it another way, don't take your Muse anywhere you wouldn't take your dog, that sainted dog of your childhood. That said…

4 DO NOT TAKE YOUR MUSE TO THE VET'S

For starters, they'll get all nervous in the car and then when you get closer they'll start to emit an incredibly high-pitched keening sound that feels like it's going to make your ears bleed (and you will never get them there in time, and if you do there's nothing the vet will be able to do anyway, trust me, oh I remember) and then if you do somehow wrestle them in they start to pick fights with all the other Muses and that high-pitched keening sets all of the dogs off too and then the receptionist and the vet and the burly handlers all start bleeding out of their ears and you realize you are too and your Muse is cross-eyed with rage and kicking the shit out of some romance novelist's pasty little Muse over there in the corner while the creative non-fiction Muses have formed a ring around them and are taking bets and by the time you've dragged your Muse the hell out of there you just don't even want to think about writing ever again.

5 DO NOT TAKE YOUR MUSE TO YOUR REUNION

I mean, my advice would be to skip the whole thing altogether, high school or college, fifth or fiftieth, but maybe you're feeling cocky, maybe you feel like you've actually accomplished something and want to show everybody how wrong they always were about you, IN! YOUR! FACE! Okay, but I'm telling you, bringing the Muse will be a bad idea. First thing, the Muse is up there at the bar slugging back five dollar drinks and doing peanut tricks for the other Muses, telling everyone how you really got that idea for that best-selling novel, hinting around that parts of it were plagiarized, and how you never really perform well, especially not after a few drinks, and by the way you seem to be perpetually about three drinks into any given situation and your talent is quite small anyway, and how if they only knew, if they! Only! KNEW! And that's when the Muse throws a drink in your face and walks out and you run after, begging now, everyone at the reunion able to hear you begging for the Muse to come back, don't leave, I need you, I'm sorry, I'll get prosthetics for my talent, just don't go.

Not that I'm speaking from experience. But why take a chance?

EXERCISES

1 Draw your Muse. Hold your drawing very close to your face and sort of unfocus your eyes and then slowly pull the drawing away from your face. What hidden pictures emerge?

2 Spend ten minutes trying to come up with anagrams for the word *muse*. What have the results of your efforts taught you about the nature of Muses?

3 If you are currently Museless, go trolling down at the local Poet's Bar. Poetry Muses are always disgruntled, secretly longing for the big bucks a fictioneer will surely make. Flash a lot of money around. Talk a lot about best-seller lists and movie options. Caution: jilted poets can be dangerous.

CHAPTER THREE:
EXPOSITION

As we agreed in the ultra-brief and thus marvelously effective (wouldn't you say, darling reader?) Chapter One, plot is everything; plot will dominate the fiction of the future like a leather-clad New York dominatrix. Plot rules! As surely everyone must by now know the inverted checkmark (exposition, conflict, complication, crisis, resolution), I will not belabor the universally absorbed. Instead, I will say a few words about each element in separate chapters, and will probably sprinkle those chapters through this book like nuggets of chocolate in Double Fudge Chocolate ice cream (which I haven't eaten since Penelope left me). There's a reason for structuring the book in this way, though it's not quite clear in my head yet, and my Muse is not much help in general and is against this project specifically, and is thereby responsible for the relative lack of sparkle or coherence evidenced thus far.

Anyhow, exposition.

Exposition is like medicine: some kinds taste better than other kinds but there's no disguising its "it's-good-for-you-ness." It can occur at any time, but usually happens early, in quick doses. Whenever it occurs, exposition is the really boring but necessary part of every story or novel in which you present to your readers necessary background material and try to trick them into thinking that it's interesting.

If my life were a story (and what a sad, boring story it would be!), how far back would I have to go? Yesterday? The collapsing house, the disappearing wife and daughters, the birth of said daughters, the marriage to said woman, our courtship, our first meeting? Back before Penelope, to those days of self loathing, my apparent fear of commitment, drinking as if I were still in college, getting complacent about my career, my life? The dry stutter of my words then? My growing certainty that I was, in fact, not a very nice person, or that I was a person without a center?

Further back, to my first failures after my first successes, the derision my second collection met with (and yes, God yes, *Different People in Different Cars* was a bad book—you did not read it here first!), the impatiently stifled collective yawn that met my first deeply flawed novel, *I Brake for Small Animals*? To Tom Wolfe crowning me the "King of Smart-Ass Fiction," starting my first and last literary feud? To my first real teaching jobs, my first failed relationships? To the white buzz of those first Jonesin' years? Back, to my essentially typical college days, when I plunged into literature and partying in almost equal measure? To my essentially unhappy teenage years? Further back yet, to my essentially happy childhood, my loving and thoughtful family? To that October day when my dog, our family pet, a telepathic mutt of dimensionless kindness and bravery, was killed before my horrified eyes? Would you need to know that my infinitely noble precognitive dog had foreseen this moment and still met it fiercely? Would you need to know that he had attempted to communicate such knowledge to me, but I, eight years old, had smiled and hugged him and heard but not listened? That I instead tossed his favorite ball (a bright orange tennis ball, semi-new and still lively) long and high, that he chased it, that it took a bad bounce near the road? Do you need to know the rest? Would you need to know that my elegant, gifted dog leaped the hedge to fulfill my desire that he fetch, that he twisted in mid-leap to look back at me one last time, with immeasurable sadness and forgiveness? Have you already anticipated the squeal of the brakes of the U.S. Postal truck? Do you have in your ears the sound of the thud, the slap and crunch? Can you see the inevitable kinetic image of the ball bouncing languidly down the road until it dribbles to a rest by the neighbors' mailbox?

And would this explain all the blandly sordid dimensions of my adult life, pre-Penelope? I drank so much, wrote so little, had become increasingly impatient with my students, not enough of whom seemed to really care about themselves or their writing, even as I realized that I didn't really care too much for myself or my writing. Said realization only further embittering me. I had written two collections of stories and one novel. Was my best book written when I was twenty-four? Would I never write another good

book? And was I going to go from one screwed-up relationship to another? Were my students going to go by on
a conveyor belt? Was this all there was? It didn't help me
to see the same mid-career burn-out singeing some of my
colleagues—in fact, my contempt for them and their flings
and their alcoholism and the easy bitter lilt of their cyni-
cism just made it worse. It's no fucking comfort to know
that your angst is boringly ordinary. Would I have to tell
you all of that before I then told you about Penelope? And
would you need some illustration of just how nauseated I
was with myself?

Probably you would. The woman I was with just prior to
Penelope was an ex-student from several semesters previous who believed that she had been abducted by aliens
frequently as a child and still was on a regular basis. This
was early nineties—1991? 1992? I forget so much from
those days, that dark time. She was a coke-head asthmatic
and when she stood me up (frequently) she said with a
straight face she'd been on the Mother Ship. For all I know
she was. She would often disappear at parties, though
sometimes suspiciously just at the same time as other
significantly younger and buffer guys would also disappear.
I would seethe and drink and stumble home stiff-legged
and mumbling to myself. On those dark nights I would
sway in my chair and try to write. All that would crackle up
out of me were images: "the wind turning the leaves palm-
up just before the storm last night" I would type, or, "there
are cockroaches in my typewriter" (which was sometimes
true).

Other times, the UFO girl, semi- or quasi-agoraphobic, would refuse to leave my apartment for days or at least until her coke and my booze ran out (I still had some Jonesin' money—why was I even living in such a dank apartment?) She waitressed and waited for something or someone better to come along. I did in fact in Carver homage drink booze out of her bellybutton, but only once, and through a straw. She did in fact snort lines off of my stomach, through the same straw. As a student she had been a sometimes brilliant writer, an always careless critiquer, a frustratingly erratic classroom presence, and then she quit writing altogether. Hunched towards the wall and feigning sleep, her back curled to me, the ridge of her spine red, she scribbled notes on my bedroom wall, then erased them, over and over. Sometimes I would get up and type a phrase and print it out and ball it up and toss it toward the bedroom, the rustle of crumpled paper like coughs rising up from the floor. We scribbled and crumpled. We did not talk much. We had sex. As a lover she was erratic and often absent-spirited, though again, she had a pretty good excuse. Eventually she quit our relationship altogether, quit town, quit (perhaps, who knows?) the universe itself. Who could blame her? It's not like this solar system had ever done much for her anyway. Lord knows I didn't. (Not that this is a book about me—the above and below is purely instructive, lissome readers.)

You see how boring exposition is, by the way?

I first met Penelope at a Science Fiction and Comic Book convention in Birmingham, Alabama. (This was just after the UFO Girl called from out of town to tell me she had, by the way, moved, sorry not to say so sooner, just before I never heard from her again. In the background I heard muffled voices, a disturbing clicking, the hum of something powerful and electronic. "You'll never ever ever get it," she said, and then the line went abruptly dead and static raged in my ear.) Penelope. Oh, my Penelope. I, a comic book fan — (well, darling reader, we all have our guilty pleasures—ask Alice Adams about the Walt Kelly clown painting collection or Robb Forman Dew about her obsession with colonial coasters, or James Lee Burke about his devotion to the Spice Girls)—I was dressed as Troll Boy, kid sidekick to Troll God. July: I sweltered in my strips of orange fur and my Troll-Sword bruised my left hip and my Troll Utility Belt chafed really unpleasantly. *Troll God* was *the* hot comic book that year, and the room was plenty full of other Troll Boys and Troll Gods. The Troll Boys were busy trying to sabotage each others' costumes — cutting off each others' troll-tails or unraveling strategically-placed fur-bits or bending a troll-ear. The costume competition wasn't until four o'clock. The Troll Gods were worse, coming up behind the various Troll Boys and lifting them into the air in great gusto-laden "troll hugs." I was paranoid and hungover and vaguely heartsick, flipping through back issues of *The Troll Team* when something quick flitted across my peripheral vision and I ducked sideways fearing more troll hugs and looked across the room and saw her. Oh, Penelope.

She was disguised as The Sprite, the radiant and unrequited object of Troll Boy's passion, a swirl of pastel and gauze and pink limbs not three tables away from me. It was the most artful costume I'd ever seen, perfect really, more a function of presence than cloth. She filled the room. I swear, as I watched, more and then more fan-boys drifting between us, she seemed to rise in the air, and drift away.

And I followed her. So did a growing number of Troll-Boys. They elbowed each other and hissed and tripped and tried to pretend they hadn't even seen her, that they were cool, that they weren't following a beautiful woman at a comic-book convention, that they hadn't totally objectified her, that they weren't as they moved and jostled and bit each other actually in anything like *pursuit*.

But they were, and so was I, and it was just after I'd elbowed a gray-haired and now-wheezing Troll Boy in the throat that a worm-herd of self disgust wiggled through my veins. The room started to shimmer, brightly. It was what alcoholics call a moment of clarity. I stopped. I grew still. My heart slowed, and slowly I smiled. I watched as the Troll Boy pack degenerated into a Troll Boy brawl and Penelope drifted away, green and blue ribbons trailing after her to the food court. The Troll Boys were wrestling and punching, spraying snot and blood and spit, rolling on the floor, knocking over a dealer's table full of vintage Star Trek models. A clot of Troll Gods came over and tried to break things up and of course only made things worse, bellowing their battle cry "*Avaunt ye naught!!*" and trying to Troll-hug into submission the nearest scrabbling Troll Boy. I saw security guards amassing from across the room. I walked to the left, shedding my troll ears. I dropped my troll sword and my utility belt as I circled the Troll Brawl, stripped fur from my arms and my chest as I approached the food court,

I tugged the fur from my feet and approached her in only my loincloth where she stood at the nacho stand.

"Who's that trip-trapping over my bridge?" I said as I stood beside her and lifted two fingers for two orders of Human Torch Spicy Cheese Nachos. My voice was rusty, as if I had not used it in weeks. I realized with a shiver that I had not, really, except to say "Hello" when the UFO Girl called to say goodbye.

"I think it's a pack of horny adolescent geek-boys," she said. "Nice loincloth."

"Nice gossamer," I said.

Two be-costumed fools we were, clinging to a simpler time, a pure adolescence we probably never had. We fell into deep like (I will not cheapen what came later by calling what we had on that day love) over nachos and a theoretical discussion of the Star Wars character as super hero (Luke's wielding of the Force as telekinesis remarkably similar to Jean Gray's mutant powers—both tempted by larger spiritual forces) which led to a shared universe theory that could have revolutionized the entertainment industry, had anybody but us cared.

"What do you do when you're not almost-revolutionizing the entertainment industry?" I said. I was always good at beginnings.

In response she smiled, and leaned forward, and pulled a Boba Fett action figure from my nose. She put it on the table. Then she leaned forward and pulled a Supergirl action figure from my ear, which she also placed on the table. Then she passed her arm over them and they were gone and in their places was a bouquet of flowers and a white dove. The dove picked up the bouquet and flew off over the crowd of still-brawling Troll Boys.

"I will always respect you," I said.

She was a professional magician, though she no longer performed, but spent most of her time inventing tricks for famous magicians. She was tired of the road, she said. She wanted to settle down. And oh, how my heart leapt in abrupt sympathy when she said that—I, too, wanted to settle down! I had not until that moment known I was unsettled.

Our first dates were full of whimsy and conversation. We went to circuses and carnivals and magic acts and revivals of Rocky Horror. In and out of costume, we shed personas and adopted identities as we circled each other, heady with love. God, did we talk. It was as if all of my words had been stopped up, choking my lungs. As if my ears had been sealed. The more mundane the subject, the more lovely our conversations—in our mouths, small talk was art, art talk almost a religious experience. Not that we only used our mouths for talk. Our first kiss happened under the grandstand at the circus, the smell of animals and sawdust swarming our senses. After we saw the act of an ex-rival magician (she told me how all his tricks were done), we went back to my place (so generic it shall always be merely "my place") and made love like a series of card tricks, revealing ourselves deliriously, unexpectedly. Later, she pulled coins and flowers from the air and we ate off of each others' naked bodies by the light of the refrigerator. I shall not shame you with the exquisite details of our athleticism. I shall not embitter you by describing the hours we spent reading, walking, listening to music together, intoxicated with each others' intellects. I shall not nauseate you by fulminating over the ways our souls entwined, two night blooming flowers in full blossom, petals brushing relentlessly, roots caressing in the darkness of soil.

Let me just say that we fell in love.

In honor of the insistence of my first-ex-editor, a memory: The first time Penelope cooked for me. The room lit with candles. Penelope in a blue dress and a green apron, her hair held back with a green and yellow hairband. Candlelight at twilight, the light changeable. I swallowed a first bite of stew so like my mother's that I had to close my eyes. It was as if time slid backwards down my throat and I was seven again, in the house of my childhood, where I belonged, the grandfather clock tocktocktocking, the dark wood polished and the murmur of my parents (tock) a lullaby as I drifted from the dinner table to the couch between my parents warm as they murmured (tock) as the television spilled cheerful blue light into the room as I dozed in my footsie jammies betwixt them (tock) as they held me carried me tucked me in stroked my hair turned out the light. And I opened my eyes and knew that somehow I had moved from like to love, and that it was with Penelope that I belonged.

Another memory, in honor of my second-ex-editor (tock) who "enh"-ed at the first memory:

Moving out of the apartment I semi-shared with the UFO Girl and into my first place with Penelope (see Chapter Seven: Setting). Penelope cleaning the bathroom. I in the bedroom, packing the last clothes, folding the last sheets, moving the bed away from the wall prior to disassembly. Seeing there on the wall down low in pencil these words, in the UFO Girl's scribble: "dark strips of starlit sky my bandages don't pull them off don't look." And beneath them an untidy pile of candy wrappers and peanut shells and used dental floss.

"I love you for the dangers you have passed," Penelope said from the doorway, still wearing yellow gloves, the toilet scrubber dripping in her hand. "Almost done?"

I pushed the bed back against the wall. "I love you that you do pity them," I said. I turned and kissed her. "Let's go start a life together somewhere," I said.

Okay, exposition sucks, and I've always been bad at it. All this lurching through time, this struggle to sort out scene and character and place. Let me offer you two suggestions and get the hell out of this chapter. Dear, sweet reader, forgive me—I promise to atone for my sins just pages hence!

Suggestion One: Skip it. Start with conflict and never look back. Does anybody really want to know much more than the bare essentials? Answer, no. They want to get to the good stuff, the human fucking misery, and get there fast, baby. So get there. In the fiction of the future, remember, what happens is always more important than whom it happens to.

Suggestion Two: Dress It Up Purty. If you just can't escape certain bare bone facts, try at least to make them glossy and weird and interesting. I had more to say about this in an earlier draft of the book, written in my little study next to the nursery, back when Penelope and I were still together and our first daughter Chloe woke up every two hours to be fed, to coo and slurp in her mother's arms, but my then-editor suggested I cut it. I did, and now I can't get it back. Now, in the now, here at the Moon Winx Motel, thinking about those first weeks and months with Penelope fills me so full of remorse and sadness I want to bang my head against the wall or put my fist through the monitor, the screen I'm looking at, my own dim reflection behind the words. I can't get anything back. How could I have been so careless with love? How could I have been so cavalier with my words?

My Muse just gave me a kick in the shin. "Write or get off the pot," she says, never removing her headphones, returning to a mildewed paperback copy of *Fiction and the Figures of Life* she got from God knows where, not my library, for sure.

Anyway, scratch suggestion two. My advice about exposition is to skip as much of it as you can. Go directly to Conflict.

If you want to read about what makes a startling conflict, go to Chapter Six. Before we can discuss that, though, and before we learn all there is to know about character and setting (as you will need people in your stories, and they will need to be someplace, before you can make their lives a living hell), we should take some time to discuss a few more nuts and bolts—audience, and purpose, and working environments, and other crucial components to the writing life.

EXERCISES

1 Think about your own life. Where would the story of your life start? What is the first moment of real action? How much of it is necessary to the telling of that moment? Condense those necessary bits to a sentence. Write that sentence.

2 Think of exposition as *exposing*—secrets, bodies, that which is usually covered. Write expository scenes as if it was the juiciest, most scandalous gossip imaginable. Better still, write as if it were a form of public exhibitionism. How much would you reveal in public? Where? Write that.

3 Begin the first sentence of your story with the words "Once upon a time..." and don't end the sentence until you've gotten all necessary expository material out of the way.

4 Sometimes I hear the words expository but I think suppository, which makes me imagine unhappy childhoods stuffed up the butts of constipated adults, which may not help you write at all, I just thought I should mention it. No, wait, this could be an exercise: What do the words expository or exposition remind you of? Write a paragraph about that. Ruminate on all of the implications. Return to your story or novel and forget you ever read this.

CHAPTER FOUR:
AUDIENCE

Well, yes, of course, you should write with an audience in mind. If you don't have *any* reader envisioned, you can be sure your piece will not *ever* have readers, dear reader! Sweet reader, oh my dear gentle ones, you must absolutely have a very specific audience in mind as you write, and then write every single syllable as if you were whispering it into that reader's ear.

Still, most beginning writers imagine rather humdrum readers. A favorite aunt, or a loved one, or Donald Trump, or Michelle Forbes (don't you dare say "who?"). See what happens to your fiction when you imagine a more exotic audience, in more specific circumstances.

John Updike likes to imagine his readers naked, wherever they are: subway cars full of naked commuters, college classrooms in full disrobement, tens of thousands of naked housewives eating chocolate and painting their toenails and reading *Rabbit is Rich*. Interestingly, both Cotton Mather and Walt Whitman indulged in the same technique.

When I wrote my first novel, *I Brake for Small Animals*, I imagined it being read to John Glenn on the Mercury Whatever mission. More specifically, I imagined Ed Harris playing John Glenn in *The Right Stuff*, reading my book as he whiled away the hours between boring NASA experiments and neat glowing space firefly swarms.

When I revised my second (eventually abandoned) novel, I imagined reading it to Dana Delaney and an adult Claire Danes (because at the time, she was like fifteen, and I don't care if it is imaginary, it's still pedophilia, which my imagination couldn't stomach) while they licked honey off of my belly on a long lazy Saturday afternoon, empty champagne bottles scattered around the bed. Then Penelope walked in, and she did not join us, as you might expect, it being my imagination and all, but instead threw a bottle of fire ants on my belly. (Then I burned the manuscript. Sometimes that's the only thing to do to a book.)

I wrote parts of this book for the cast of *The Cosby Show*, which I watched obsessively in reruns. The first season was the best, and losing Lisa Bonet was a deathblow to the middle seasons, but the last two seasons are full of fine character moments and good acting and are vastly underrated. "Cos, this chapter is for you!" I would shout at the television as I sat down to write. "Cos, baby, that metaphor was all for you!"

(This was just after Penelope left me. I almost dedicated this book to Bill Cosby. Right now it's being written without dedication.)

You can get even more creative. Write to Winston Churchill, late in his life, painting naked in his country home, depressed but stoical. Write for Marilyn Monroe when she's still Norma Jean Whatever, on the bus to Hollywood, you in the next seat, both of you jumpy with caffeine and possibility. Write for Kathy Acker while she lies on the table about to get her first tattoo. Write for Madison Smartt Bell, shooting pool in a dark bar in Alabama, tired and lonely, just before another drunk graduate student asks him to prove he really knows martial arts, which he does, with an almost-apologetic roundhouse kick to the student's temple. Write for Richard Nixon, two minutes from death. Write for my friend Katie Riegel where she sleeps in C F S-related exhaustion on a long weekday afternoon, her golden retrievers snoring at the foot of the bed, a perfect phrase taking shape in the sweet gray light at the back of the mind or a fold of the sheet. Write for Emily Dickinson, a baby, four months old, in her crib at dawn, cooing at the light as it slants in her window, the whole house still and asleep. Write for James Wright, hungover and miserable on a brilliant fall day, smoking cigarette after cigarette in the back yard of good friends he's visiting, refusing to come back inside.

Dear sweet sainted reader, you get the picture.

Once one has one's audience firmly lodged in one's mind, then one must begin to consider purpose. When I lived in

Alabama, there used to be a Sunday morning show on one of the local religious channels called "Jumping for Jesus." Frighteningly well-scrubbed teenagers wearing white tee shirts and blue jeans climbed up on an enormous trampoline and jumped for hours on end while viewers called in pledges. (The girls were all flat-chested and I suspect strapped down too, and the boys were all underendowed and apparently wearing jockstraps and briefs under their blue jeans, to avoid any prurient appeal to the show.)

We would watch this show, sometimes, the UFO Girl and I, as night bled to morning and we sat on the couch shaking and glassy eyed, popping valiums, the shades pulled, the lights off. The sound turned down, we watched them jumping, regularly, wholesomely, their faces pink from scrubbing and holy exertion. The UFO Girl would snuffle, begin to cry. "I used to have a trampoline," she would say each Sunday, as if she had not said it the Sunday before. "I used to love to bounce."

I would sit there and smoke, wired and paranoid.

"I used to love to bounce, until the aliens snatched me right out of the air."

I had no words for that. The way she said it made me want to check the window shades.

"Those bastards," she said. "They even stole bouncing from me. There's nothing left."

Let me tell you, by the end, we were all suffering, the Jesus jumpers and the UFO girl and me too, waiting for unconsciousness as I lit another cigarette and another and another. It seemed like there was no end to the jumping one could do for Jesus. When I would wake up later, cigarettes burned to ashes in the ashtray or on the coffee table, there would be a red-faced preacher waving a Bible and I would have no idea how long he had been there. I was too lazy or too afraid to check the TV listings. Sometimes the UFO Girl would be there, sleeping noisily; sometimes she would be gone. Vanished.

Anyhow, the question to ask yourself as a writer is, what would *you* jump for? Would it be for Jesus? Would it be for money? How much money? Would you jump for a nice dinner? For world peace? Would you jump for days on end to get back the wife and the children you love? Would you jump for a clump of bananas? Would you jump to reclaim the childhood that had been stolen from you? Would you jump to get Gilligan off of that island forever?

One time, in the middle of a backyard croquet game with Don DeLillo, Thomas Pynchon, J.D. Salinger, Andrew Shay, myself, and I believe Grace Paley (there were so many croquet games those summers), the question of purpose came up. It was evening, the shadows long and the sky deepening towards night.

"I write for love," Andrew Shay said, gravely, looking out at the unmown fields, then up at the house. Oh, how we chuckled at that! Poor Andrew. He wore khaki shorts and dark socks and white sneakers and a black pocketed tee shirt with a toothbrush head peeking out. He brushed his teeth obsessively, ten or twenty times a day, and always stank of mint. He had nice teeth, though.

Even in the twilight we could see that he blushed, and Paley (or was it Cynthia Ozick? Alicia Griswold? Rita Mae Brown? Time has bent my memory.) shushed us as we giggled and the outdoor lights snapped on and Penelope appeared in an upstairs window to watch and we played on well into the night. It was Jayne Anne Phillips, I think, and the chief giggler was Mark Richard.

I digress. Whatever your answer is, *that* is what you should write for. (Even love, if you must.) Pretend every sentence is a bounce on that trampoline. That's your purpose. Never forget that you need one!

EXERCISES

1 Write a paragraph for the Pope about a balloon popping. Now describe the same thing for your grandmother. Now rewrite the paragraph for a two year old who loves balloons. Now write it one more time for a child who hates balloons. Now write it again for an audience of your own choosing.

2 List the things that you want most in the world. Look at your list. What could you write to fulfill every item on that list? Write that. Be happy.

3 What's the worst reason for writing? Think about it. Then write a short story to fulfill that motivation. It wasn't as hard as you thought it was, was it? Repeat as necessary.

CHAPTER FIVE:
WORKING
ENVIRONMENTS

Back when I would appear at conferences or go to summer writing workshops, I used to get frequent questions about how I worked: do you write with a pen or a pencil or do you work on the computer? What room do you work in? Do you need music in the background? These questions used to sadden me. At first I thought that those who asked suspected there was some secret formula—if they could just replicate Gus Jones's working conditions, why, then, they could write like Gus Jones! And yet, as we talked, I discovered that these people knew the working habits of hundreds of writers—that Dickens would write on a stepladder, that the Brontës would take turns writing on each other's backs, that Hawthorne would write in a tub of ice water. It wasn't that they wanted to write like Gus Jones, or anyone else, really—it was that they would rather picture writers at work than actually do the work of writing. And that worries me, winsome readers, oh, it troubles me. I don't want you to get so caught up in the mechanics of environment that you forget to write!

And yet I know too that there *are* certain things that I do now, regularly, to help me write. And I know that there was a period when I got cocky and ignored my own "rules," and I know how adversely that affected my writing.

For a time, when I was first married to Penelope, I thought that I could write anywhere. I would take notes longhand in a lawn chair in the back yard, or type on a manual typewriter on a board and two sawhorses in the basement, or on a laptop on the hot tar roof, or carve notes with a penknife on the floor beneath the bed by the light of a flashlight while Penelope, my love, my life, slept peacefully above me. I could and did write with a ketchup bottle on my naked body, with cookie dough shaped and baked, with a jackhammer on a city street, with a lawnmower and a neglected lawn. Oh, hubris!

I had abandoned all of the work habits that had served me over the years, my rules. I was blinded by love and thus overconfident, and I ignored those rules with the defiance that is nurtured by love, tender love, the love that feeds all strong foolishness. I believed that I could dare anything, do anything, and so wrote anywhere, any old way. Words poured out of me, readers, and my Muse was there nurturing me, and I was giddy with love—I thought that meant that those words would be beautiful. I did not pay attention to the rules.

What follows are the rules that I should never have abandoned, the laws I'm still struggling to reimpose on my writing life. Note that every writer has her or his own set of rules, from Plato to Antonya Nelson, Sophocles to Sandy Huss (though Sandy's rules change with each new phase of the moon, they are still her rules, and she does still obey them) to Gloria Naylor to Michael Martone to Junot Diaz to David Wright.

Here are mine, and those of some other writers I love and admire:

1 MUSIC

I only write if I have James Brown doing the long version of "Cold Sweat" on a tape loop, and the cassette on auto-reverse. If this is absolutely impossible, then I allow myself to substitute the soundtrack of "The Sound of Music." These are the only two options that work for me.

2 LIGHT

Eschew light. Anyone can write if they can see what they're doing. After Penelope and the girls left, and I was faced with so many hours of quiet and emptiness, I found I needed to become much stricter in my approach to writing, or I wouldn't do it at all. I wouldn't do anything at all, ever again. So I returned to the method of composition I used for my first stories, and type all of my drafts blind-folded, with the computer monitor turned off. As an extra challenge, I will not sit down to write until I've had a few drinks. There are times when I wish I had learned to touch-type, but I find that deciphering drafts on the next go-around actually lends a certain edge to my stories. Some obscure passages I leave as is. Did you know that Faulkner invented over one hundred words? Shakespeare invented many more (note to self: check these facts). Sometimes poor typing can lead easily to prose innovation.

3 AIR

Breathing is necessary. Your air should have life-sustaining oxygen in it. If you find yourself writing in a low-oxygen environment, at the top of a mountain, say, or at the bottom of a mineshaft, I'd recommend a tank of oxygen. Some writers I know—Erica Jong is a notable example—keep a tank of oxygen with them at all times. I know one writer who used to keep a tank of nitrous oxide near his typewriter, but my second-ex-editor informed me that I can not tell you who he was due to ever-stricter libel laws in this country. In any case, if you are serious about your craft, you will need to keep breathing.

One writer who may have been an exception to this was William S. Burroughs, whom I always suspected of being undead, but now that he's un-undead we won't ever really know for sure. Anne Rice would like you to think that she can eschew oxygen for the same reason, but I've seen her on the streets of New Orleans sucking away at an oxygen mask she kept strapped around her face.

Some writers like to scent their oxygen—Peter Taylor was fond of a nice sort of lilac potpourri, John Cheever liked the smell of pine burning, Matt Devens couldn't write without the smell of bacon and eggs cooking, Don Hendrie, Jr craved the smell of crushed rose petals, and Anton Chekov was fond of Calvin Klein's Obsession (see 1 above re: anachronisms).

Personally, I like air-conditioned air, even in winter.

4 DISCOMFORT

I'd suggest either being as comfortable as humanly possible or as uncomfortable as humanly possible, but don't go halfway either way. I like to write while sitting on broken glass and nails, wearing a wool shirt and woolen trousers with no underwear, with clamps on my nipples and testicles, but that's just me. This doesn't work for everyone, especially if you don't have testicles. Flexibility is allowed on this point.

On the other hand, my great good friend Allen Wier prefers to be be-cushioned and perfumed and oiled and fanned, a fleet of manicurists and pedicurists and epicurists hovering just behind his impossibly comfortable Barc-O-Lounger.

5 ROOM

I've found that my writing rooms must be exactly fifteen feet by eighteen feet with ceilings ten feet high. Coincidentally, these are the dimensions of my room at the Moon Winx Motel.

6 TEMPERATURE

Avoid moderate temperatures. I like to keep my writing areas very very cold, and then strip down to my boxers. This coldness keeps my nipples erect, which I find important, especially when I'm writing poetry. Some writers, though, will crank up the heat and wear thermal underwear and several layers and parkas and scarves and sometimes gloves, though this makes it more difficult to type. Not only do they craft some fine fiction, but they generally shed a few pounds in the process.

Obviously, writers who find themselves in particularly hot or cold climates have an advantage over those of us who live in moderate or fluctuating climates. This might explain the success of Jack London, for example. Yet it is surprising how few young writers pick up stakes and move to Alaska or some small country along the equator.

The wise young writer will take heed!

7 VIEWS

There is a famous novelist who writes fiction about men and women who live in trailer parks and drives a BMW (he points proudly to his own trailer park past, though often neglects to mention its duration, which was sixty days) who insists on what he calls "doing the Bartleby." He can only write facing a window that looks out on a brick wall. He has erected brick walls in front of the study windows at his country home in Massachusetts, and has had a brick Colonial built right next to his place in upstate New York. This may seem a little bit extreme, but it points to the importance that many people place on their views. Some need them, some hate them, some choose studies carefully based on their views, some write in windowless basements. Some paint bars on their bay windows, or Dantean tableaux, or pornographic images, or cartoon characters chasing each other. Some paint pornographic cartoon characters chasing each other through Dantean tableaux as seen through the bars of a prison cell.

On this issue, I couldn't care less. A view is nice. So is no view. Some things are important, but this—who cares? It's not ever been an essential requirement for my Writing Life either way. "Doing a Bartleby" indeed.

8 FOOD

When I've really gotten going on a story, I only eat little cocktail weenies from casserole dishes, smothered in that great cocktail sauce like Celia Kingsbury always served them in (there have been cocktail weenies in every culture, in all times, but none have ever been as good as Celia's— she'd bring them to every MFA party, and I always swore I'd mention them in a book). Make sure the dish is kept warm, and do not use your fingers or toothpicks, but lean over and pick them up with your teeth and /or tongue. Keep your hands clean at all times—your hands are your livelihood! How else would you type?

A word of advice: do not ever eat Cheetos while writing. The orange stuff gets all over your fingers and you'll have to pause often to suck them clean and even then they'll still be sticky and leave a little orange residue on your keyboard and after a while you can still taste them at the back of your throat, only the taste has gone sort of sour somehow and thick besides, and if you spit experimentally on the floor beside your chair your spit will be orange and now you have disgusting orange spit on the floor, and they get caught in your teeth and if you pick the caught parts out with a fingernail, you'll stain your fingernail, which looks hideous and embarrassingly unhygienic, and what if someone picks that moment to knock at your door and introduce themselves and you have to shake hands, or worse, what if you forget about it and go out later and meet some pretty someone of the opposite or same sex and give said someone a smile that is still florescent and wave a languid orange-stained hand in the air—God, just thinking about it you'll have to get up to wash your hands and clip your nails and brush your teeth and by the time you get back you'll have forgotten what you were writing about and will have to end the chapter, probably abruptly, and probably a few pages short.

You'll realize, too, that no rule will ever bring back what's been lost. Nothing will ever order your disorder.

EXERCISES

1 If you write using a computer or word processor, only write during thunderstorms. To add even more urgency to the process, run an extension cord outside during the next thunderstorm and write with your bare feet in a baby pool full of water. Foil hat optional.

2 Buy a broken chair. Try to fix that chair. Keep adjusting and fiddling with that chair until it's just right. As soon as it's just right, ask yourself if you hear a squeak when you sit down. Sit down often to test. Was that a wobble when you stood up? Stand up and down frequently. When you're sure that there's no squeak or wobble, realize that your chair is ugly, and buy a new broken chair. Do not discard the old chair. Store it in the basement. Maybe it wasn't so ugly after all.

3 Write blindfolded and ear-plugged and nose-stuffed in the dark, on a computer whose monitor is broken. Never look at anything you've written later. Will it all to your children when you die. Become posthumously famous.

CHAPTER SIX:
CONFLICT

Conflict arises at the moment in a story when the desires of a main character are first opposed.

Face it, my lovely but bloodthirsty readers, you've been craving this moment. You wouldn't be human if you didn't pine for disruption, commotion, misfortune. As long as it belongs to somebody else, it's cathartic, soul- and mind-enriching. Other people's individual troubles, if written properly, ennoble the race. And et cetera, and thus forth, and so on.

Don't make me do this.

If I could in any way control the shape or flow of memory, dear readers, I would gladly go comatose and dwell forever in the early years of our marriage. I tell you, our wedding was perfection—deeply spiritual, intensely moving, awesome in its beauty. Penelope never looked more lovely, and I, well shaven and scrubbed and coifed and aftershaved was, for the only day it mattered, handsome. At the reception the food inspired many odes of joy, the music somehow managed to leave deeply pleased all ages and types, the liquor was not just plentiful but free. Our parents sat together and became fast friends for life. Our unattached siblings found there the loves of their lives. Our divorced friends reunited with their ex-spouses. I'm always irked at those who namedrop unnecessarily (as opposed to yours truly, who does so always necessarily, as my hang-gliding pals Jamaica Kincaid, John Fowles, Art Spiegelman and Pam Houston often remark), so I will not bore you with the guest list, a veritable who's who of contemporary literature. Okay, an example: at a table near the kitchen sat David Foster Wallace, Anne Lamott, Peter Ho Davies, John L'Heureux, Mark Costello, Stephen Wright, Valerie Martin, Elizabeth McCracken, and Jeanette Winterson— and they all got along. Even Bill Dessoffy, just the tiniest bit tipsy, was welcomed to the table when he wandered over bearing *Wall Street Journals* for everyone. I mention this only to suggest the wondrousness of the conversation, though as in any gathering of writers, the dancing left a little bit to be desired (particularly unnerving, I was told later, was the Locomotion conga line led by Philip Gambone). Penelope and I did not notice (well, okay, we noticed Ethan Canin doing the Hustle, but only just barely). The room was giddy with light. I felt as if we were at the center of a beautiful and slow-moving tornado, still in the stillness there, rapt, devoted, gorging on each others' presence.

We did not notice that Inman Majors was passed out underneath the table that held our wedding cake, or that

Chitra Divakaruni tied his shoelaces together. I did not see and would not have understood why Rick Barefield and Dan Childress cut off his tie and lit matches in his shoes.

We did not notice, I swear to you, the craps game that started up near the kitchen doors—if you told me Rob Trucks was there, or Richard Price, or Ron Hansen, or Jim Harrison, I'd have to take your word for it.

So enraptured was I of every pearly word that dropped from Penelope's sugared tongue that I did not notice the non-conversation at the table with my parents and hers.

That posse Ira Sungkrungrun led to the kitchen, Amy Tan and William Trevor and Robert B. Parker and Laura Esquivel? I swear we only heard later how they reduced the caterers to tears, took over the kitchen, and began to cook for all those assembled.

The only music I heard that day was Penelope's sweet voice—I did not hear my college buddies Bob Zaiser and Morgan Whittier and Tim Johnson and Frank Crane as they choloroformed the band members one by one and took up their instruments and started thunking through a raggedy version of "I Want to Hold Your Hand." I was positively shocked when I was told all of this later.

I did not know that my friend Jim Jones (unrelated) unplugged their amps, though in retrospect I can guess why.

For all I saw that day was Penelope, radiant. I could not let her leave my arms, even to eat, and on this perfect day we had no use for toilets or mouthwash. There was no hail that day. No thunder, no rain. Nobody wept lonesome in a bathroom stall. Everybody's skin was clear and their pasts unblemished and their presents excruciatingly pleasant, their futures grand with possibility. So this was what it was to be happy, to be normal. As we scurried to our car (decorated and tin-canned by Mailer and Vidal) I tried to imagine a wedding that magnificent with, say, the UFO Girl as the bride. A dark shudder seized me, then fled. I barely watched the road as I drove to the airport. The only thing I wanted to see was Penelope, in white. The car was not so much parked as abandoned. There were no crowds, no lines, no delays, no crying babies on the plane. The honeymoon, a carnal month in southern climes, was more blissful and creative than any celebration of human union should be. And did this bliss abate when we resumed our everyday lives, I back to my one-one teaching load at a prestigious southern university and Penelope back to her workrooms to invent ever more fantastic tricks? You know it did not.

Oh, dear reader, don't make me do this.

Those magic weeks piled up like snow, deep drifts of hours and days and weeks and months that were pure and cool and tall and untouched by soot and grime. Those months, then a year, and then two, and we moved twice to ever better houses. Penelope invented a trick by which she seemed to juggle the dining room set, eight chairs and a table, plus two leaves, without any effort. She sold this trick to David Copperfield, though he did not use our dining set when he later performed it. We bought a place in the country. We settled in for the long haul. We began talking nurseries, trust funds, retirement annuities. We made love spectacularly. Dare I say with artistry, born of purpose? It was such a swooning relief to feel purposeful—to feel normal. That sense of purpose was rewarded, not once but twice in the next four years, first Chloe Elizabeth Jones and then Miranda Joy Jones, and oh our ecstasy was thorough, backwards and forwards we were in our bliss.

Dear sweet readers, don't make me do this.

Can we not, in the fiction of the future, embrace a fiction without conflict? Can we not explore the subtleties of untrammeled happiness? Can we not begin with happily ever after? As my fellow ornithologists Rick Bass, Audrey Petty, Joan Didion, Robert Olen Butler and Cathy Day might cry out in unison, cheek to cheek, can we not be Happy Fictioneers?

No, of course not. Eden's no fun if it doesn't fall. Paradise doesn't mean anything if it's not lost.

Let me suggest that on the honeymoon, then, there was always a bottle of champagne. Let me float the notion that her tricks flummoxed me in ways I could not fathom. Let us imagine a day on that honeymoon that does, truly, foreshadow all that is to come:

It is gorgeous, this day, warm and breezy, the air heavy with the exotic scents of flowers and oils and sands. She is gorgeous this day, topless in a sarong and a lei, flowers in her hair. They are on the balcony of their luxury room at their luxury resort. Ocean view. The sound of the surf below. The sun about to set. They'd made love an hour ago, showered together, dried and perfumed each other. He is happily suntanned, leaning against the balcony railing. She sits in a chaise lounge, her feet up on the railing on either side of him.

"Do you trust me?" she says, mischievously.

"With my life," he says. He sips his champagne, grins down at her.

"You have to believe absolutely," she says.

"You're my religion," he says. He sips his champagne, lifts an eyebrow, grins.

"Close your eyes," she says. And he does.

There is a momentary feeling of weightlessness, a brief and terrible flip of his stomach, and he almost drops his champagne glass. He opens his eyes, startled, and they are on the beach. He looks up and sees their balcony, empty. She puts her arms around him. He turns in her arms, sees the sun drop spectacularly into the sea.

"Ta-da," she says.

But he is shaken. He has no words for this moment. He closes his eyes again, tightly. He hears her say his name. Eyes still closed, he turns, begins to walk away down the beach. Only when he is ten paces away does he open his eyes. His vision has gone dark, swarming with spots. He leaves her there, crestfallen. She blames herself, curses herself, it's all her fault. He keeps his champagne glass long after he's drained it dry. When he returns, she is in bed, crying. He goes to the little desk there and takes a few notes for a story he later writes and sells to *Harper's*. Then he puts the glass down and returns to bed and kisses her and apologizes, and she apologizes, and they make up, and make love, and they do not fight again the whole honeymoon or many days and weeks and months and years after.

But from that day forward, she keeps her best tricks to herself, and he does not ask to see them, ever.

EXERCISES

1 Write a conflict that is Person vs Animal (worm, tapir, narwhale, vole). Make the animal the protagonist. Set the story on another planet.

2 Write a haunted house story in which there is no house and there is no story.

3 Write a story about your most painful childhood trauma. Change your gender. Change your age. Change your ethnicity. Change the year. Change the trauma. Everything else is true.

4 Write a twenty-page story in which your protagonist gets everything he or she wants. Make this story a tragedy.

5 Write a story about a person in conflict with his or her own sweat. Set this story in the South. Avoid allegory or irony.

6 Imagine your life is a novel. What's the central conflict? How do you think it will be resolved? Save yourself millions in therapy. Send half of that to me, care of the Moon Winx Motel.

7 Do you think Shakespeare would have written about the Kennedys were he alive today? What would be the central conflict of *JFK?* Compare and contrast to Oliver Stone's movie. Discuss.

PART TWO

Write

"Get away from me, you evil men of writing."
—Larry Johnson, to reporters

CHAPTER SEVEN:
SETTING

You may not have ever really thought about it, but all stories are set someplace. I have never read a story that took place nowhere. Even an extra-dimensional void is someplace. Try to picture "no place." When I do it, I visualize this sort of white expanse, like an infinite margin with no text, and characters floating and tumbling around—but they float and tumble in this white expanse. Maybe your no place is a black expanse, but you still have characters there—you see? I had to use the word "there" to describe that "nowhere."

Right now, as I type this, I am sitting at a circular, slightly wobbly table next to the bed in Room 6 of the Moon Winx Motel. I'm typing on a Performa 6200, which my wife apparently didn't want when she left, as I found it later in the trunk of my car with no recollection of putting it there, along with a battered croquet mallet and a mint copy of *X-Men* #108. The curtains here are a dark blue and brown pattern, and are today drawn, so that the room is really only lit by my computer's monitor, which keeps going all fizzly and used to drive me crazy until I apparently got used to it, because I hadn't really thought about it until just now. Now it's driving me crazy again. I wish I hadn't just thought about that. You'd be surprised how often I say that.

Anyway, setting: the curtains are heavy and drawn, the room is dark, the furniture is scratched and blocky, the bed is middle-saggy, the bedspread dark dark blue, the TV bolted to the dresser and the nicest thing about the room— thirty-two channels though no free HBO. The air conditioner is the second-best thing about the room—I have it going full blast all the time, and I sit around in my underwear and a bathrobe and eat take-out pizza and chicken and teach two nights a week and write this book to you, most gently esteemed readers. Once a day, a maid comes by to clean the room and change the towels. She has a nametag, but every day it says a different name. I never know what to call her. On this day, she was Susan and she also changed the sheets. When she does this, I try to leave the room, to give her some time, plus it's embarrassing to have a stranger touch your soiled linens. Not *soiled* soiled, just ordinarily soiled, but still. As I have no place to go, though, I generally just wander down to the room that passes for a lobby and watch TV with what's-his-name the desk clerk. It doesn't matter how long I give her, whenever I come back she's never quite done, and I have to stand awkwardly in the doorway or sit on the toilet or a corner of the bed, depending on what's been left undone. We rarely speak, but we smile a lot, very pleasantly.

My Muse is here when the maid is not. Just now she's lying on the bed, painting her toenails black and listening to Esquerita: she whispers along, something about loving the life she's living. My Muse looks at me inscrutably, often. I turn back to the monitor and you, oh my readers, always.

So what does setting tell us about character? What is symbolic about the passage above?

You tell me. That's real life, and I'm damned if I can figure it out. But let me show you how a writer of the future will take boring old real life settings and really *use* them!

Those scratches on the furniture, first of all, barely mentioned by me, are not just random scratches, but the carvings of various previous dwellers. On my desktop and the arms of my chair are sundry and assorted declarations of love, mystery and intrigue. INVADE HOLLAND VIA JNX. PAT LOVES CHRIS. THERE IS NO HERE HERE. 32-16-78. QUAIL CARBON SIX. LET BE BE FINALE OF SEEM. I HATE MY LEFT INDEX FINGER. SHUTTER SPEED 1/36TH. MILK BREAD EGGS JUICE GRAPES. YOU CAN'T GO TO VEGAS AGAIN. Oh, what fun the skillful writer could have with such details! Could they be used as symbolic? Yes! Could they build atmosphere? They just did! Could they, perhaps, be plot points? They aren't, but they could be!

In the room of the future, the curtains open slowly, and sunlight floods the room, and out in the parking lot we are stunned at first to see a boat glide backwards by. What on earth? As the viewer, some man, watches and waits a pickup truck comes backing into view, and we realize that this is another fisherman pulling in to the motel after a long day of fishing. As the boat and the truck pass we see the swimming pool on the far side of the motel, and the pot bellied Ray-Banned Midwestern father and mother standing on either side of the diving board with their hands on their hips and their tender plump tummies outthrust, watching as their bored and most probably stoned daughter dives into the deep end again and again, climbs out dripping and bedewed, her dark hair slick, adjusting her green bikini bottom with two thumbs, walking past her parents whose eyes are studiously not on her adjusting her bikini bottom as she steps up on the board and strides once-twice-step-leap past them, twisting in the air and vanishing into the blue with hardly a splash, a few quick spits of water all that the man can see from his table as his Muse clucks in weary disgust and begins to paint the toenails on her other foot and he pauses, his fingers on the keyboard, and looks out at the world as interpreted by the Moon Winx Motel.

And see how wonderfully the twin moments of incongruity, of boat and of pool, surprised us? And see how the symbolic implications of voyeurism begin to unroll? That's the magic of setting!

In the setting of the future, a long line of ants moves along the dresser behind the television. They are small, and red, and each carries a grain of food in his or her mandibles. But what kind of food is it? And where are they taking it? Setting opens doors!

In the future, pretty blue and yellow flowers will sprout in the dirt of the corners, and tiny penguins and polar bears will blow cold breath by the air conditioner that thrums all night, and the saggy bed will enfold the man in the middle of the night, like two gentle hands curling around him, holding and rocking him while he sleeps and dreams of girls clad in green bikinis diving off of boats that sail through the sky.

Setting, dear readers. Never neglect your sense of place.

When I think of my life with Penelope, I think first of houses, the houses we lived in. By the end of my relationship with UFO Girl I had pissed away most of the money from my first few books, so we did not then live too lavishly. If I were going to write a novel about that life (note to self: consider other examples? Must we worm our way back and back and back to that life?), I would try to catch first the places we lived, our first rental apartment together, the top floor in a falling-apart house that shifted ominously in the storms and tornadoes that seemed to wrack Alabama in our first years together. Previous tenants had tried to burn the leaves that had gathered on the tiny tin porch outside of the front hall window and had set the walls of the house on fire, a fact we discovered only later when some of the paint in that hall chipped off and we saw the charred wood beneath and realized our landlord had just painted over the burnt walls, which would have explained the faint barbecue odor we caught on some warm days. And yet we lived there for a year, making love during those storms while the house pitched and yawed, adding another coat of paint to the burnt walls when necessary, sweeping the leaves off the tiny tin porch, cuddling naked by the air conditioner. Now was that love or some baseline laziness, some fear of change or confrontation? And yet I swear after a while I did not see the char, smelled it only in my sleep. In dreams. When we did finally move, it was to the ground floor apartment, which was more spacious and smelled better, and did not sway quite so much. When we finally moved into a house of our own, the landlord gave us a first edition Faulkner as a parting gift because we were such good tenants (i.e., because we did not complain). So what does place tell you about us, dear reader? Can you see the hairline cracks in our marriage?

As we moved to bigger and bigger houses, our marriage became more and more pinched. Is this just ironic? Or could our love only thrive in mildew and char, water damage and poor insulation? Our next place was the rental house on 13th Street, across from the Vietnam vet. We were flanked by a venomous older couple and a house full of revolving frat boys and sorority girls. The whole neighborhood was loud and volatile, the vet coming over to the frat house frequently with a grenade in one hand and the pin in his teeth, mumbling that they'd better fucking shut up or he'd fucking well shut them the fuck up forever, Penelope and I not knowing whether to call the police or cheer. The cadaverous old man next door forced their trembling poodle to poop on our front lawn each night at dusk, which poop I would then scoop up and deposit on their front lawn, finding out only later (a digression: when I was writing the autobiographical novel *A Banjo On My Knee,* the one I wound up burning, I revisited the old neighborhoods and interviewed all of my neighbors, which would have solved a lot of problems for me had I done something like it when they were actually my neighbors) that he thought that poop was from *our* dog and that was why he made *his* dog poop on our lawn. When I informed Mr Kelley that we'd had no dog back then, he just shrugged and said, "Sure, not that we could *see*." And Penelope and I in a structurally sound house that needed maybe a few coats of paint and maybe one or two lawnmowings more than we seemed to get around to (we had no lawnmower but relied on the men (mostly African-American) who came through the neighborhoods with lawnmowers in tow and who charged next to nothing but always caught us on days when we had literally not a single dime in the house, though we checked, and held them up, at which point we felt bad and invited them in for iced tea, probably more out of middle-class guilt than any genuinely friendly impulse, though we (Penelope surely) were always genuinely friendly in those days and some days would sit with some of these men for more than an hour talking about whatever, though we could have gotten to a bank and back by then with enough to pay them to cut the grass and maybe do some landscaping, but, well, by that point it seemed like too much trouble, and we'd catch them next time, right? "Right," they'd say. "Thanks for the tea, y'all." (Note to self: why do so few white writers make race their subject? And what about you? How many of those "people in cars" were black?))

From there we bought the place in the country, a big old ex-farmhouse, surrounded by high grass, infested with various vermin and in an almost-constant need of repair. It was here that we spent the longest period of our married life, in a house that became some sort of weird halfway house for disgruntled writers and insecure writing students, which was another kind of volatile altogether. This was my fault, of course. In those days before Chloe was born I told myself that I wanted to share the bliss of our marriage, extend it—I was always inviting visiting writers to stay with us, and always inviting students current and ex out to the house, and pretty soon word got out that there was a sort of standing invite at our place, and writers would drop by all the time with twelve-packs and bottles of vodka and croquet sets and badminton nets and in the long hot summers there seemed to always be a party going on and I admit to being half in the bag myself most days and nights and I must further risk your good opinion of me by telling you, oh my readers, that my wife did not approve. Who would? Vicious and hungover writers (invariably male) afraid they'd written their last good book years ago staggering out of their bedrooms in their underwear at noon only to confront tongue-tied and trembling writing students so desperate to make a good impression they said the most idiotic things I've ever heard human beings say to other human beings: "I love the stains on your boxers, is that a sort of conceptual statement?" "Oh, you like coffee too? Here, have mine." "Hi, were you one of Gus's students in the old days?" (This last said by Andrew Shay, who somehow overcame his social ineptness and became famous.) So you can see what I mean by "volatile." During one particularly nasty croquet game my dear good friend Margaret Atwood went into the house, got some lighter fluid, doused her mallet, and flung it at my other dear good friend Tama Janowitz for "sending her away" without apparent need or provocation (my Muse here looks at me disapprovingly, but that's how I remember it, and that's how I'll tell it, by God), only all involved were drunk, and the mallet instead grazed Andrew Shay and did not set any part of him aflame (the fire went out mid-fling) but did give him a terrific knock in the head and Penelope had to take him inside and give him five stitches and keep him awake for several hours in case of concussion (and so they drank coffee and hot tea with lemon and did jumping jacks and whenever I went inside for more beer they would be red faced and breathless and Shay would say "caffeine" and Penelope would say "calisthenics" and I would shrug and carry armfuls of beer outside where we continued our game, more civilly, though a mallet short).

Oh, she wrapped her chagrin around her like a stole, Penelope did, and wore it everywhere, on the hottest days especially, and I, besotted, eyeballed her chagrin and smiled with false benignity and cracked another beer and went outside to pour more drinks. Reader, what can I say? If I had it do over again... well, see Chapter the Last: Denouement.

I hang my head in shame. Something was terribly wrong with me. You see how much setting can tell you about even the most mundane subject? Sometimes setting is just backdrop—a passing truck, a diving girl, a stained bedspread. But that house was where our marriage resided. All of those places are filled with Penelope and will be always, no matter what they've become, whether they're still standing or not. No matter what you say.

EXERCISES

1 Picture your childhood house. Now picture a bulldozer plowing through your childhood house. Now describe your childhood house, post-demolition. What sorts of wonderful story opportunities does this description suggest?

2 Think about the room you're sitting in, and the way you would describe it. Now think about that room if some essential component was removed from it: the floor, or the ceiling, or light, or oxygen. Now write a page about a character walking into that room. What would happen? What happens to your description of that room?

3 Take a set of characters and put them in an unlikely environment: the O.J. Simpson trial in a Warner Bros. cartoon world, a Supreme Court deliberation in Yankee Stadium, a Yankees fan at the ballet (can you tell I'm a Red Sox fan?—*salut,* Tim O'Brien!), a ballet company on the space station Mir. What results in the tension between character and setting? Can you explore any dramatic (not comedic) possibilities?

CHAPTER EIGHT: PLOTS TO AVOID

Speaking of conflict [NOTE: as Gus's manuscript was scattered across the floor of his motel room, it may be that certain chapters appear out of order—A.S.], there are certain questions of plot that must now be raised. I hope that you do not flinch at the unflinching honesty to follow. You know I love and care about you, cherished readers.

To write our way past the next millennium, we must come up with new and exciting plots. This can be more difficult than it seems for the novice writer. In my many years of teaching creative writing at just about every level, I've seen many, many stories and, inevitably, many, many very similar plots. It is always sad, of course, to see the beginning writer come in beaming, sure that he or she has found the freshest, most fabulous story idea—only to have that story be yet another variation on the same old story I've been reading for years. This can be discouraging, not to mention a waste of precious energy and time. To avoid just such a situation, I've listed below the eight most common plots, those that should be avoided at all costs:

1 YOUR LOVER TURNS OUT TO BE A GIANT EARTH-WORM FROM THE CENTER OF THE EARTH AND EATS YOUR DOG, FOR WHICH YOU CAN NEVER FORGIVE HER.

There are many variations on this plot. Once I had a particularly bad workshop, and saw this same plot, in slightly different guises, at least eight times. One man would just change the lover's origin point: the center of the earth, the dark side of the moon, the fourth dimension. One woman in the same semester could only change what the lover ate: a parakeet in one story, three goldfish in another. "Stop!" I cried to them at the last. "It's the same damn story!" They didn't listen. It was maddening, distracting. My own writing suffered for a good year or two because I couldn't get the permutations of that plot out of my head: earthworm, slug, ground squirrel; earth's core, north pole, Mars; dog, kitten, gerbil. At one point I even wrote a story about an ex-lover who turned out to be a giant mosquito from the Amazon and ate a poor ex-significant-other's seeing-eye dog (he was blind, of course), for which he *did* finally forgive her (but Penelope was still with me, then, and my fiction was more hopeful). Writers-to-Be, a Lesson: Bad Plots happen even to the best of us. Sometimes the more you read, the more they happen. Recognizing them is the difficult part.

2 THE SAD CLOWN WHO CHUCKS IT ALL TO BECOME A DEPARTMENT STORE SANTA CLAUS AND THERE MEETS THE LOVE OF HIS LIFE IN THE HALLMARK

SHOP.

But, of course, underneath his happy white beard, he can't scrub away the sad clown frown. My darling friend Nanci Kincaid once said to me, "Gus, if I have to read one more sad-clown-turns-into-Santa story, I'm going to break down and cry." And not because of pathos, dear reader. Avoid sad fictive clowns. If you must write about them for some reason, if you were raised by sad clowns, or were a sad clown once yourself, then for God's sake, I beg you, do *not* set your story at Christmastime. Even Robert Coover could not write the clown-at-Christmastime story, long though he may have tried. If *you* try, your readers will resent you. Reader resentment is something you should attempt to avoid.

I once had a student who courted reader resentment. She wrote very realistic stories that always ended in the Hallmark Shop. Sometimes in the collectibles section, sometimes near the Mahogany line, sometimes near the rack of graduation cards. Oh, we all hated her. You've never seen such venom in a workshop! Afterwards, of course, we would all buy each other drinks, and get falling-down drunk, and forgive her her shortcomings. In the mornings, though, bleary-eyed and ashamed, we still hated her. Remember, Future Writers: you can take things too far, in fiction and in life! Her name was Sarah something. I don't know what happened to her. We lost touch after that semester—she got married, or got a job, or some such thing. Remember—perseverance is crucial!

3 YOUR DOG REVEALS, TELEPATHICALLY, THAT

YOU'VE SET UP YOUR CROQUET COURSE ON HIS SCENT-SCULPTURE ENTITLED "CANINES IN GETHSEMANE," AN ACTION ROUGHLY AKIN TO TAKING A RAZOR TO THE MONA LISA, AND NOW DOGS THE NEIGHBORHOOD WIDE ARE ANGRY AND COMING YOUR WAY.

If the fact that Homer, Shakespeare, and Bocaccio have all worked variations on this same basic conflict doesn't deter you, just think about the many times in recent years we've seen this story in the headlines. When art can only feebly echo the latest newscast, might I suggest that perhaps it's not art at all?

I once taught with a young writer named Tim Parrish who went out of his way to steal ideas just like this from small-town newspapers and journals of paranormal phenomenon. He would publish them almost unaltered: a name change here, some fancy language inserted throughout, a few details shuffled. When art is so similar to things that are not art, don't both cease to exist? A warning.

4 THE PATHETIC MIDDLE-AGED WRITER IN LONELY ISOLATION DRINKING TOO MUCH AND SMOKING TOO MUCH AND ENGAGING IN TOO TOO MUCH INTROSPECTION AND GENERALLY MAUDLIN OR IRRITATING BEHAVIOR, UM, DOES SOMETHING UNUSUAL.

This situation is stale and unworkable on several levels. First, it's not even really a plot. Second, academic fiction is never very interesting to the average reader. Third, it strains credibility in too many different ways. Most readers hate

whiners, and hate white middle-to-upper class sexist bastards who bemoan the death of Western (read white
middle-class male) culture. And don't think that subtle
variations—say, making him an Ancient Celt named
HeadCleaver, or a gay Aborigine on walkabout—makes
any difference at all. How could you ever find a way to make
such a figure interesting? The very thought of it makes me
shudder. No more, dear readers, no more. Avoid such
mustiness in your fiction.

I, myself, used to work hard to avoid mustiness, both in
my writing and in my life, as, of course, one feeds the other.
Yet it is a struggle. When I first settled into my life with
Penelope, and my Muse began to purr and coo, I thought
I had been saved from must forever. Of course my—what
is the word I'm looking for? shallowness? complacency?—
my somethingness later betrayed me.

Here in the here and now, staring at the aggressively
bland walls of my motel room, I find that I am surrounded
by the stink of must. No offense to Julie the maid. I'm certainly a contributor to the problem, as I am back up to a
pack or two a day. Cigarettes are clearly a major source of
mustiness, and while you may be drawn to the romantic
notion of writers chain-smoking in dark bars or by their
word processors, resist it. Instead, power-walk at the local
mall. Make up a new name for yourself and find a way to
introduce yourself to a stranger—using your new name!
My dear good friend Lee Smith suggests eating bran
muffins and bicycling every day. My other dear good friend
Allison Joseph, a poet, searches every lawn she is on for
four-leaf clovers. (You should make friends who are writ-

ers, by the way—they will have many good ideas for you!)
Charles Baxter, for example, believes in going to county
fairs and petting the little goats. Had I a goat handy, I
believe I would be much less musty. Or musty in a totally
different way. Guard against the wrong kind of mustiness:
any or all of the techniques mentioned above will inject
freshness into your life, and into your fiction, too.

5 THE GAY SURFER WHO FALLS IN LOVE WITH HIS
FATHER WHO FALLS IN LOVE WITH HIS SON'S LOVER
WHO FALLS IN LOVE WITH THE PERKY HETERO-
SEXUAL GIRL NEXT DOOR.

Can you say *Othello,* anyone? (Note to self: or is this *Mid-
summer Night's Dream?* Try not to confuse the two in the
future.) How many muscles have to ripple before we can
call that body clichéd? How many hands have to tremble
on how many undrawn swords? How many urges must be
repressed before we gasp at the contortions that result?
Yawn, dear reader, yawn and turn the page.

6 ANGRY AT THE FAMILY DOG, THERE ONCE WAS A
LITTLE BOY OR GIRL WHO WISHED HE/SHE COULD
ENTER THE NATIVITY CRECHE AND WAKES UP
CHRISTMAS MORNING AS ONE OF THE WISE
(WO)MEN, FROZEN WITH MYRHH IN HAND, AND
CAN'T SPEAK, AND HAS TO WATCH HIS/HER BROTH-
ERS AND SISTERS OPEN ALL OF THEIR PRESENTS AND
THEN LOOKS AT THE OTHER NATIVITY FIGURES AND
REALIZES THEY ARE VAMPIRES, EVEN MARY AND THE

BABY JESUS, AND THEY CAN MOVE.

Some students get so impatient with me when I tell them this is old news, been done, ancient history. "Mr Jones, you don't ever offer up any suggestions for what's new!" they wail. "How can we ever come up with anything new? We're asking!" I wish it were that simple, dear writers, I do! If only my answers would work for you! But you must realize: it's not the destination but the journey that counts, and we must all make that lonely fictive journey alone, with nothing but our computers and our wits to guide us.

In the year that I won Teacher of the Year at the University of Alabama (I can not quite remember the year) I actually came to blows with a student named Tony Earley over this very plot. I'd been having a bad semester in a sort of vaguely existential way, and the UFO Girl had made me stay up all night with her sitting in separate lawn chairs in the back yard, staring up at the cloudy sky until dawn with not even a brief sexual interlude to refresh us, and matters of staleness were thus on my mind that night in workshop, so perhaps I was more blunt than I normally would have been. I told young Mr Earley, in no uncertain terms, that this was one of the oldest stories out there, that he had not brought anything fresh to it. He insisted he had made it up just two days before. I conceded that that might very well have been true, but that what he made up two days ago had been done to death almost since the first crèche. He persisted in misunderstanding me, thinking I was accusing him of plagiarism. The class stared at us, slack jawed and uneasy. I threw a piece of chalk at him, and he leapt across the table and attempted to assault me. The rest is neither here nor there. He has since gone on to publish widely, beautiful stories of a very real South, and we get together every now and then and have a cup of coffee and laugh about our tiff. So, a dual lesson: 1 what you think is new may not be new, and 2 persist! Persist and you will one day have drinks with writers you tried to punch out.

7 THE MAN WHO SAVED TIGER WOODS FROM DEATH BECOMES OBSESSED WITH THE IDEA THAT ALIEN BEINGS LIVE BENEATH GOLF COURSES, JUST WAITING FOR INNOCENT, SOLITARY GOLFERS TO REACH THEIR HANDS INTO THE CUP SO THAT THEY CAN GNAW THEM OFF, THUS RAISING THE INNOCENT GOLFER'S HANDICAP CONSIDERABLY.

I first heard about this plot from a writer named Tom Chiarella (I think), who never actually wrote the story. I wanted to steal the idea and write the story (whomever I first heard it from), but never actually did, because I later heard so many people talking about it, and I realized it was old because so many people knew about it, and even if it has never actually been written down, it's already been done so many times in people's heads that you have to ask yourself, what's the point? Then it got turned into a movie and made a gazillion dollars and I was kicking myself for days, but never mind that, dear ones.

I even dreamed this story, more than once. Writers of the future, beware: stories that come in dreams may seem clever or even unique but the exact opposite is almost always true. Nobody wants to hear your dreams. That's why they are dreams, and occur only in your head, at night, when you are asleep.

About stealing: every writer steals, and the good ones do it well. The bad ones don't do it well, and so never get published. One of my first teachers, Terry Hummer, said something like that to me, and I'm sure he got it from somewhere else. I used to borrow many ideas from my wife, ideas she whispered to me at night after we'd made love. "Once upon a time," she would say as the sweat dried on her skin, "there was a husband who was afraid of mirrors. One day a young woodcutter seduced his wife and led her to the Forest of Mirrors. What do you think the husband did next?" I would promise to think about it. And I whispered many ideas to her, which she was free to steal, though how she could have incorporated them into her next magic trick is admittedly beyond the power of my mind's stomach to digest. Future Writers, everyone knows that if you live with a writer or are friends with a writer, everything you say and do is fuel for the old creative bonfire. That's why they're with you! Friends and lovers secretly love to see their ideas in print!

One way to get a lot of ideas is to volunteer to work on the literary magazine at your school or in your community, or to start your own literary magazine. Don't plagiarize, of course, but sometimes you will see a good idea so clumsily executed that it is almost a moral imperative that you take that idea and do justice to it. Teaching creative writing is another sure way to get a lot of ideas. See Plot 1 above for the danger there.

8 YOU CAN'T FACE THE THOUGHT OF YOUR DYING

GRANDMOTHER SO YOU SEND YOUR DOG TO SIT BY
HER SIDE AND HE FALLS IN LOVE WITH THE NIGHT
NURSE, WHO IS NOT A NIGHT NURSE AT ALL BUT
JOHN TRAVOLTA IN DRAG, DOING RESEARCH FOR HIS
NEXT MOVIE, AND HE ADOPTS YOUR DOG AND THEY
LIVE HAPPILY EVER AFTER ON THE MONEY YOUR
GRANDMOTHER LEFT TO HIM IN A LAST-MINUTE
CHANGE TO HER WILL.

The difficulty here, as in all of these plots, is what can you bring to it that's new? Of course all stories have been told, but some stories offer more room to work in. Stories are like closets. Some of them are big, and have oodles of space, undiscovered shelves and shoe racks. You can put all sorts of your own stuff there. So even if the closet is old, the stuff in it is all new. Others are tiny and cramped, so small you can't even walk into them, and really can't hang much that's your own there at all. And who really wants to work in a closet that can only really hold your uncle's out-of-fashion suit and your mother's old Easter hats? John-Travolta-in-drag stories are like small closets. Stay out of them.

I have other words of advice about plot, of course. Avoid stories that have dogs in them. People are tired of reading about dogs. Metafiction is not fiction at all—I think John Gardner said this first—and has no real sense of character or plot, and so should be avoided altogether. It is, finally, to use the polite term, mental masturbation (note to self: ask that Romantics professor whose office was next to yours who first said this phrase, and to whom), and while that may be good if you're lonely or socially inept, it's terrible if you want to have a relationship with your readers. With anyone. Avoid it. What is socially relevant today is the Morton Downey, Jr show (note: Rikki Lake is hotter now (note to self: insert name of hot abrasive talk show host here)) of tomorrow—avoid relevance. Read a lot. Write a lot. You'll start to get a feel for what's old and what's new. As we crash into the next millennium, search your hearts. Find something new in there, and squeeze it onto the page. It may be bloody, but it will be fresh. It doesn't matter how many broken relationships you go through, how many bitter still moments you ache through in the middle of the night. Search the seepage of your hearts. If you do that carefully enough, enough times, you will become a writer, and isn't that all you've ever wanted? What else is there to understand?

EXERCISES

1 Plot the perfect fictive wedding. Who will be on the guest list? Where will the conflict begin? What food will be served? Will the honeymoon contain the complication or the climax?

2 Imagine that you are a thousand years old and live a thousand years in the future. What plots will you have read over and over again in the last (next) thousand years? What will seem new and unusual to you?

3 See how many different ways you can make the following things central to the plots of your stories:

> a gorilla suit
> a dog
> a wedding cake
> a smashed guitar
> a car with rich Corinthian leather
> Green Lantern's power ring
> a motel swimming pool
> a Weber One-Touch grill
> a stamp placed upside down on an envelope
> a rubber glove
> a razor blade

Bonus points for making them all vital plot devices!

CHAPTER NINE:
CREATING
CHARACTER

As we have discussed, the fiction of the future will be primarily driven by plot, which is as it should be. Things that happen matter! Or things that matter should happen. But they still have to happen or matter to people, darling readers. You can try to write stories without characters but it doesn't work very well, and even the passive voice will not carry you for much more than a chapter or three: "The car was driven down the road. Then a tree was collided with. Then an explosion was witnessed. The still-flaming wreckage was towed away." Pretty soon, your readers will wish they knew who had been barbecued in that car, and who had to do the towing, and did he or she know there was a burnt corpse in that car, anyway? I mean, wouldn't you check first? Character creation just solves problems for the busy writer.

LIKEABLE CHARACTERS

I think writers should stop worrying about this. You'll never create a character that will be universally liked, so why bother? Why make this a concern? Similarly, going out of your way to make a character *un*likable seems wrongheaded.

A much better consideration is born of the obvious pun: is this character *lickable?* If you can imagine licking the character, and enjoying the experience, then that character is probably fit hero/heroine material. You can further complicate this test by imagining degrees of lickability. A lick on the forearm is not quite the same as a lick between the toes, or the armpit (among other places—use your imagination!).

If you can't imagine doing this to your characters, try this test out on the people you know. Penelope, for example, I could imagine licking everywhere, every last inch, as a form of worship. The UFO Girl, on the other hand, I could frankly only imagine licking (forgive me, delicate readers) between her legs, which I did often enough. Her feet were always dirty, though, and she often came to my apartment reeking of cigarettes and stale beer and sweat and her nose was always running and in all, that portion of her seemed the least hygienically challenged. I would prefer not to lick most of my friends—I can't really imagine licking my dear good Monopoly chums Charles Baxter or T.C. Boyle or Allison Baker or Lorrie Moore or Thom Jones. Oh, perhaps a lick on the nose for William Styron.

If you can't imagine licking this or that character, or can't imagine doing so without being repulsed, then you can be sure your reluctance will come through to your reader.

This may be a problem for the writer who, like me, can imagine licking *all* of his characters (who, unlike people, will not have an immediate reaction you would have to deal with should you choose to test lickability), every place imaginable. Think of this, then, as a strength: your fiction will later be praised for its moral complexity.

CHARACTER DESCRIPTION

The most important thing to get right about a character is the externals. Other people might tell you to focus on nailing the conflict or writing up a psychological profile or inventing a childhood (or adulthood for your child characters), but that's all nonsense. As if the traumatic death of a beloved, telepathic, precognitive dog could explain anything about anyone.

In truth, most people make up their minds about people in the first five minutes after they've met them in real life, and the same will be true of your characters. And the easiest way to make your mind up about someone is to make value judgments about their appearances. You might often be wrong, but that's real life—this is fiction, and we can make the appearance mirror the reality of the character. Your readers will jump to conclusions anyway, just like they do in real life, so this is obviously the most effective way to fix your characters in your readers' minds.

For example, if I told you that the UFO Girl dressed mostly in tin foil bras and panties, with cellophane wrapped around her legs and arms and midriff, her hands and feet in baggies affixed with rubber bands, on her head a pyramidal tinfoil hat, what conclusions would you jump to? Would you know immediately that she believed she was an abductee? Would you think that she was unusual, different, bizarre? And yet, one time I went with her to her support group meeting and everyone there was dressed similarly. Some of them wore the tinfoil outside of their cellophane. Some of their hats were more conical. But she was not unique—in fact, she was conformist, I realized.

At the meeting itself, everyone said roughly the same thing: "Hi, I'm Jane/John Doe. I'm an abductee." And we all said, "Hi, John/Jane Doe." And then s/he would say, "I was first taken when I was seven when I was in bed. They paralyzed me, then lifted me out of the open window, and spirited me aboard their ship." And we would all nod and smile and murmur supportively. My girlfriend would whisper "Yessss, yesss, yesss" after each sentence. Then various probings and interviews and humiliations would be detailed. And when it was over, we would stand and applaud, for what I'm not sure.

When it was my turn, I stood, and said, "Hi, I'm Gus Jones, and I've never been abducted." And they all said, "You will be, Gus, you will be." I didn't know what to say to that, so I sat down. Their tinfoil rustled. They looked at me as if sizing me up, and one began to whisper into his cellophane sleeve, and I began to shake with paranoia and couldn't stop looking at the closed door. I never went back to a meeting, although now I know how much support the UFO Girl could have used.

So anyway, you can see that appearances do in fact lead one to make assessments about character. In real life, sometimes the judgments we leap to are erroneous. In fiction, they don't have to be. It's like my old fishing pals Donald Barthelme and Andre Dubus and Ralph Ellison and Dick Yates used to say: "Sometimes, appearances can be deceiving."

And anyway, in the future, people will not look like or dress like people of this day and age, so why try to be realistic in your description of your characters?

For example, I think that one fad of the future will be clown make-up—everyone who's young and hip will put on clown make-up, different looks for different moods. If I ever finish this book, I think I will write a not-at-all-autobiographical novel (note to self: call it A Crying-on-the-Inside Kind of Clown?) in which all of the characters will wear clown shoes and red noses and elaborate, ritualistic clown make-up. In this book, everyone from stockbroker to gradeschooler to grandmother will be into clown fashion. Anticipate the future, gentle readers!

And what dramatic possibilities will open up for me! Instead of telling you that Gustav and Shantain, my sympathetically dysfunctional antagonists, are feeling murderously amphetaminized, I could instead tell you that they paint their faces green and black, their lips a sloppy red, their wigs a neon pink Don King style. That says it all, right there!

In the tender love scene, Ho and Kelli will strip the greasepaint from each other, an act of trust and revelation. See how description can be symbolic? (See Chapter Nineteen: Symbol Crashes.) That they then make love with their clown shoes on will show the lingering fear of commitment each has in their crazy, mixed-up world. And I won't have to explain any of this.

The climactic car chase will be made even more allusive when the Emmett Kellys pile out of their v w Bug and swarm the Red Buttonses still trapped in their Pacer. Such subtle symbolism can really put some spin on a scene that might otherwise be static.

(Note to self: run this idea by the Muse, first.)

You, too, can use description to create rich, layered characters! You can even use description as symbolism! And you can even do it without dressing them as clowns, though that certainly helped me write that novel! The point? Use your externals!

SMARTNESS

My dear good wonderful colleague Val Vogrin—or was it Toni Morrison?—used to say that characters should be as smart as they can be, meaning I guess that even if they are really stupid characters they should still be smart stupid characters so that readers don't say "That's stupid, why did he or she do that?" but say instead, "Oh, that character is stupid, but he or she is trying hard." No, it was Val Vogrin, and it's good enough advice, but I think she has missed the obvious: characters should be smarter than you are. Therefore, my characters are all rocket scientists and psychotherapists and chess prodigies and artists and mathematicians and they all have IQ's of 180 or 190 and they know more than I could ever possibly know.

This gives me something to shoot for: maybe someday I will be as smart as the characters I have created. Plus, it makes me very proud of them. Good characters, I say. Good for you for being so smart!!

In the next chapter I shall give you a useful trick for developing your characters. Now, on to the exercises!

EXERCISES

1 Remember those flip books, where pictures of astronauts and monkeys and ballerinas were cut into horizontal thirds, and you could flip tops and middles and bottoms to create weird hybrids? Try the same technique when developing your characters! Create a character who has a pretty face, a weak stomach, and big feet. Write the bio for a character who has a weak mind, pretty feet, and a big appetite. Develop nine or twelve more traits, shuffle them into three piles (top, middle, bottom), and pull a trait from each pile. Let your imaginations rocket you to the next millennium!!

2 Study your best friend. Change his or her name. Write down everything he or she has said or done for as long as you have ever known him or her. Change one important thing about his or her appearance, and one important thing about his or her past. Then put everything else into a book. Deny everything later.

3 Imagine that each of your characters was a specific kind of dinosaur: this one is a raptor, this one is an apatosaurus, this one is an allosaurus, this one is a pterodactyl. What would he or she do in a given situation? EXAMPLE: If Don Quixote had been a Tyrannosaurus Rex, what would he have done when confronted with the windmill? Apply to your own characters. (I can always tell when a writer has employed this technique: see, for example, Cormac McCarthy's *All The Pretty Horses* or Tim O'Brien's *The Things They Carried.*)

CHAPTER TEN:
QUESTIONS
OF CHARACTER

Sometimes when I am having trouble understanding one of my characters, I pretend that he or she is a real person, sitting in a lawn chair on the other side of my computer screen, sipping a beer or tea, looking up at me placidly—no, reverently—and eager to answer any question I might put to him, or her. The answers as I imagine them help me then to write the character, and when I have asked enough questions I shoo her, or him, up out of the lawn chair and back into the story at hand. Here are a few questions you might be tempted to ask, some bad, some good:

Who are you?

This is not a very helpful question to ask your characters, as they will surely be looking for you to answer this for them. As we turn to God for direction and identity, so your characters turn to you. Would God ask us who we are? He might ask us what the hell we think we're doing, and don't we ever use the brains He gave us, and what in His name possesses us sometimes, but He knows exactly who and what we are. This is one of those terrible house-of-cards questions that could collapse your novel—if the characters you've invented begin to doubt your omniscience, what does that say about your imaginative powers? Let's stop thinking about this right now, gentle readers, and ask a less perilous question.

What's your favorite color?

Surprisingly, answers to this question can be helpful. If a certain cantankerous old gentleman who recognizes and fears the onset of senility answers "blue" to me, then I know he has a wellspring of tenderness in him, that he has a romantic soul, that he swerves to avoid squirrels as he drives and will attempt to rescue baby birds that have fallen from their nests. Thank you, I will say to him, and return him to his story, where he will swerve to avoid hitting a chipmunk and slam into a telephone pole, much to his daughter's horror. Had he answered "green," I would have known that he was bitter through and through, planning to do something awful before he lost total hold on his mind, and I might have returned him to his story to let him smoosh the chipmunk on his way to his lawyer's, with whom he plotted to wrest custody of his grandson from his daughter, whom he believed to be a dope fiend because she had a prescription for Tylenol 3.

Are you bigger than a breadbox?

You would be surprised at how many of my characters answer no, but I think they become confused as they peer up at me reverently from the other side of the computer screen. I don't put much stock in their answers to this question.

My muse, however, is endlessly fascinated both by their answers and the breadbox question in general. She tabulates their responses, with variable columns for body language, vocal inflection, and facial cues, and makes pie charts and three-dimensional graphs designed to illuminate the whole breadbox issue for me. She'll snap her gum busily as she works on the bed, kicking her legs, *Exile on Main Street* blasting so loud on her Walkman I can hear every last note (my ex-editor told me (three deadlines ago, an age an eon a happy-lifetime-gone ago) that the cost of quoting a few lines of the song my muse is most often listening to is prohibitively expensive, said cost to be borne by the author (i.e., me); thus, I can only tell you that whenever I notice she seems to be about twelve seconds into track seven). She hands these charts and graphs to me with her usual boreder-than-thee bubble-pop, but I see the excited glint in her eyes. As in, "If you would just interpret this data correctly, you'd get it." I do at least pretend to study them carefully. I look long and hard. I admire the artistry of her graphwork.

Privately, she keeps a fat black notebook that classifies all things she encounters as bigger or smaller than a breadbox. She takes it with her everywhere. There are three billion entries, and she spends at least an hour every night updating it. Or used to. In the last few weeks, we haven't really left the Moon Winx much.

If you could be any animal, what would you be?

Frankly, this question bores me, and I don't know why I keep asking it, as it bores my characters, too. They would much rather consider what kind of an animal noise they would like to be (few would like to be a snake, but many would like to be a snake's hiss), or what kind of animal mating practice they would like to be (surprisingly, many gravitate toward some form of asexual reproduction), or what kind of stuffed animal they would like to be. I learn the most about them as they consider how stuffed animals would survive in the world if they were alive—what would they eat? Couch stuffing? Would they roam wild, or would they be pets, ingratiating themselves with human families? Perhaps they would roam in packs, trying to find families or young children to adopt them, clinging to their little legs, scaring them. And how would we feel about them then? My daughter Chloe used to watch videos about a young talking dog named Spot, and Spot had a teddy bear who was sometimes alive and sometimes not. Whenever it talked, though, it scared her badly, and she would ask to be held.

I still have some of those videos, and watch them, sometimes, late at night, drunk and weepy.

If you could be any drink, what would you be?

Coffee, one young woman answers, and I know that she wants to be energetic, rich, purposeful, even as her four children sap the best part of that energy, and she settles for getting by, for not making major mistakes, for making sure they have clothes on and don't fall down the well. She never regrets having children, but she misses what she once was; she misses her old energy, the days just out of high school when she painted and took a few night classes and worked as a teller at the bank and made some money and lived on her own, not even a life of high adventure, she never even wanted that, but a life of purpose, of horizons that were directions, not boundaries. Coffee, she says, a little wistfully, and I know she is also thinking about the coffee shop she used to go to every morning. The counter seat that became hers, the young handsome stranger to town who began to sit next to her, who wooed her and made love to her and married her and knocked her up, four times in seven years, years she thinks she was always pregnant or always nursing, always one of them inside of her or clamped onto her, always she was never alone. Coffee, she says, and I know.

Back to your story, I say. I'll see what I can do.

A strawberry soda, the stockbroker says, and I am not surprised that he does not say vodka martini, or perhaps Budweiser. Because when he says it I know that each night he is afraid, deep down dead afraid, of the killing pace of his life, of how little he knows about what he does, about the charade he's playing, this fucking game, how long can he keep it up? How long before they find him out? He was a Political Science major in college, for God's sake! How did he even get started down this road? How could he ever leave it? He's almost thirty, and hasn't the nerve to go back to school, and has gotten used to the house and the cars and the money, the things it buys, the occasional line of coke, the nights in the city, the big-screen television. He likes that part of it all and it scares him, too, because he knows how empty it is, how masturbatory. Strawberry soda, he says, and I know he is thinking of a day when he was twelve and he walked down to the corner drug store and bought a copy of *X-Men* #108 and a strawberry soda and walked halfway back and stopped under a tree by the banks of the Nonesuch River and sipped his soda and read his comic book. He would be a strawberry soda, he says, and I understand.

Back to your story, I say. I'm sorry things didn't work out.

Absinthe, says the little girl of seven, and I know she longs to be exotic, to surprise, an inarticulate longing that will never be fully expressed. I give her fangs and wings and send her back to her parents. Unsweetened ice tea, says the old woman with the walker, and I know she dreams of her dead husband and I send him to her in her dreams. Boilermaker, says the guy who works for Asplundh because it is what he is, and I put him in a dark corner bar with a Red Sox game on the television going late, into extra innings, and he drinks into the night, the stars drifting lazily, the moon swelling happily overhead.

If you could live your life over again, would you?

So many of my characters say yes! This infuriates me. They don't even know what horrors or happinesses are in store for them—they don't even know what all they've lived through, sometimes, if I haven't given their pasts much thought—yet again and again they say yes. That woman there with cancer says yes, though her last days will be so painful! That fellow in that story who woos his brother's fiancé and wears prosthetic limbs strapped to his healthy limbs, he says yes, happily, all of it over again. That young girl there, coming to terms with her own sexuality, struggling with the oppression of a homophobic and sexist society, she doesn't even think twice, she blinks and says yes. This one has his head between his knees as he sits in the lawn chair behind the screen, that's how sick he is at what is sure to come, and he says yes. This one has been pierced and tattooed and painted and mutilated and regrets each mark the past has lain upon her and still she looks at me balefully and says yes, every needle, every knife, bring them on again and again. Calamities unfold, sadnesses erupt. Still each one says yes. Yes, they cry, yes, yes, what else have we got?

My characters are fools.

Who do you think you're fooling?

These questions tend to come later at night, when I or they are bleary with drink, and belligerent, all of us brave because of the barrier of the computer screen. Me?! they say, listing in their lawn chairs, empty beer bottles scattered around. What about you, you sorry sack of shit? You can't even hang on to happiness when you've got it. You let a woman like Penelope and children like Chloe and Miranda just evaporate away from you, and you have the nerve to ask us a question like that? We can't take it anymore, we're out of here—which way to Kent Haruf's computer?

Would you go to bed with me?

Another late-night question, again inspired by the bravery of what can never be, the safety of the screen.

(But while I am in an imaginary bed with them I will close my imaginary eyes and imagine being with Penelope.)

You'd be surprised, by the way, by how many of my characters say yes.

How do you take your coffee?

This, the next morning, puffy eyed and embarrassed, trying to make amends. Sugar? Cream? Maybe the sunlight leers in through the windows. Maybe you've drawn the blinds. Maybe the neighbors are still wondering what the hell you do at night, anyway. Maybe you unplug all of the phones for weeks on end. Maybe your character has on sunglasses and is pacing wearily behind the lawn chair. Maybe your character has snuck off in the night to return to a Robert Stone or E.L. Doctorow novel, leaving behind a note on the lawn chair that says, "Last night was a mistake. Please don't call me again." Maybe your character dozes off in the chair and you shake him or her awake, almost tenderly. You could be nicer to them. You could try harder.

And when one of them says yes, two cream, one sugar, suddenly you know: this is the kind of character who would curse you out drunkenly then fall into bed with you, mumbling obscenities, passing out halfway through the act, leaving you shaking and alone, staring at the computer screen.

You know, then, just what you can do to them.

Now you know just what you are.

EXERCISES

1 Place yourself in escalatingly precarious positions of moral compromise. Find it harder and harder to recognize the right thing. Fail to do the right thing with increasing frequency. Write about it.

2 Imagine that you are a police detective interrogating a suspect. The bare bulb swings above. The suspect trembles/ snarls/smirks in a splintery chair. Suspected of what? You decide—aggravated plagiarism, glibness in the first degree, literary trespass. You smack your blackjack in your left palm. Your editor (three deadlines ago) watches from behind the two-way mirror, impatient for you to finally figure out the deficiencies that are perfectly obvious to her: weak motivations, one-dimensionality, stale inevitability. You circle the desk. "So," you bark. "How was your relationship with your mother? What was the most traumatic event of your childhood? If you could be any kind of tree, what would you be?" Scribble down the answers. Crack skulls when they don't come quickly. Write down the transcript of your interrogation.

3 You are a lawyer interviewing prospective jurors for a civil case. Ask if appearing in this book will cause the character undue hardship. Ask your character if he or she has any inherent doubts that the novel-writing process, while it may be flawed, is the best process we have for arriving at the truth. Ask if she or he has any biases towards any of the other characters in the book, or the author. Consider how well this potential character would work with the other

three characters empanelled. Type up the transcript of this inquiry.

4 Interview the following figures for a job at McDonald's:

> Alexander the Great
> Blanche DuBois
> Satan
> Lassie
> Billie Holiday
> Richard Nixon
> Mother Teresa
> Gordon Lish
> Ted Williams
> Joan of Arc

Write out the scene that would unfold.

5 Create a character who is something you're not: male if you're female, gay if you're straight, white if you're black, happy if you're sad, poor if you're rich, urban if you're rural. If you can not inhabit that fictional vessel, make stuff up about what you think it must be like to be any or all of those things. Put that character into a scene with an angry Rottweiler and revise several times. On the next to the last draft, change that character back into everything you are. Revise. On the last draft, change the character into a third permutation: pre-operative transsexual, Hispanic, manic-depressive, suburban middle-class. Revise. Revise. Revise.

CHAPTER ELEVEN:
DIALOGUE

I t's hard to write stories without dialogue. This is mostly true because except for those who are vocally impaired or are mentally challenged or have suffered some sort of medical complication to speech, most people talk, at least a little. Also, people get tired of reading long paragraphs, and dialogue is a good way to break things up and keep your readers turning the pages.

The problem is that the way people talk makes for really staggeringly shitty dialogue. If you listen to people for any length of time, your realize they are inarticulate, full of truly annoying speech tics, and cursed with limited vocabularies, little interest in language, and no real desire to communicate anything beyond their most brutally immediate need, if they even want to communicate at all. When I want to write dialogue, I try not to listen to actual people at all. In fact, I go out of my way to avoid hearing real people using their own real words.

If you can't turn to reality for your dialogue, where can you turn? Here I come, readers, to save the day! And here are a few ways to write really spiffy dialogue:

1 STRIP

Record what people say, if you must, and then take out every non-essential word. For example, if I said (as I often did, as I did just two days before she left me) to Penelope, "I'm going to the store, do you need anything?" that would be bad dialogue. Look at how much more compelling this line is: "Going store. Need?" That's dialogue that makes you sit up and take notice.

2 BALLOON

Instead of stripping dialogue down, inflate it in any way possible. Let's look at the same sentence, ballooned: "Hey, Penelope my love, my light, my eternal freaking flame, I'm going to take my big old baby-blue Chevy and zip on down to the all-night drugstore. Is there any possible way I can purchase or steal anything, any condiment or medicine or sweet or treat or magazine or gun or prescription drug that might make your life more comfortable or manageable in some small or large way?" This is dialogue that compels because it is richly detailed and full voiced. Sometimes more makes your readers say, "More, more, more!" Also, if you're trying to hit a specific word count for contractual or editorial purposes, this technique is a really nice shot in the arm.

3 AS SPOKEN BY

Imagine that all of your dialogue is spoken by famous actors. Not only is this a marvelous descriptive aid and screenplay shortcut, it can layer your dialogue with vibrancy and richness. Look at this exchange:

"Well, pilgrim, I've been thinking about moseying on down to the store."

"Oh, pet, pick me up some calla lilies if they're in bloom."

Your readers feel more relaxed now that they don't have to do the work of imagining people they've never seen or heard moving through places they've never been. They can settle back in their easy chairs and imagine a lost movie starring easily identifiable movie stars.

If you want to try a delightful variation on this technique, read the very next one!

4 ACTOR, ACTOR!

Write your characters as if they were classically trained actors forced to perform *Saved By the Bell*, or *Family Matters*, or any situation comedy you hold in low regard. Imagine that your story is a scene in an episode of *Baywatch*, as performed by Kenneth Branagh and Emma Thompson (note to self: buy current movie magazine and find a hot acting couple still actually together—ask Muse?):

"I'm going."
She stared at him soulfully.
"To the store."

She moved into his arms, rested her head against his bare chest, the sound of his heart and the surf pounding in one rhythm in her ear.

"I would get you something," he said. "You know I would. That is, if you wanted me to…?"

"Oh, darling," she whispered into his chest hair. "Oh. Darling."

Zing! What tension! What a merry mix! Calling Hollywood! Your next book option is on the line!

For a variation on the variation, read on, keen readers!

5 MIX GENRES

If you've written a sweet love story, write dialogue that might have come from a hard-boiled detective story. Or, if you've written a gritty crime drama, give your characters dialogue that might have come from a musical.

6 USE DIALECT FOR INVENTED ACCENTS

I agree with the conventional wisdom that says that a little bit of vernacular goes a long way, but if you invent a regional dialogue, you can put the "Cula!" back in vernacular. For example, it would be racist, I think, to have an elderly black man speak the line "Mah dogs iz tir'd." But look at how riveting this line is: "Mёe doŏgs ess téè'r'd." Readers that have no patience with tired and clichéd uses of the vernacular will be reinvigorated by your bold use of phonetic spelling and accentual punctuation.

7 TRIM TO THE EMOTIONAL CORE

Real people talk around what they want to say, or are frequently inarticulate. You can't afford to let your characters be that indirect or verbally limited, though. Instead, cut straight to the emotional core of what's being said. In real life, for example, I might have said to Penelope, "How long until dinner?" and she would have said, "About twenty minutes." Of course, what I meant was, "I'm really hungry, but I'm also hoping I have time to suck down another vodka martini before dinner." And what she would have meant was, "Since when do I do all of the cooking, anyway? You're not the man I married at all!" Of course, we both would have understood what the other meant. But how do you convey that in dialogue? How about the following exchange:

"I'm fucking starving. Where'd you put the vermouth?"
"I didn't touch your fucking vermouth. I want a divorce, you asshole."

See how much more informational that is? Dialogue should communicate what we sometimes only communicate through body language, inflection, or lawyers.

8 PUNCTUATE

Okay, it's probably not advisable to end every sentence with an exclamation point. That's the mark of a real amateur. But what about every word? "I'm! Going! To! The! Store! Do! You! Need! Anything!?" Wow! Your readers will be on the edges of their seats. Get creative—with—your—punctuation…(see what I just did for emphasis there??? (and there?!))

Want a character who speaks loudly? Steal from John Irving: "I'M GOING TO THE STORE!"

A soft-spoken character? " …(i'm going to the store)…"

An uncertain character? "I'm? Going? To the? Store?"

These are just a few suggestions. There are many ways to write a single line, to unspool the truth through dialogue. Two days before Penelope left me, I did actually say, "I'm going to the store. Do you need anything?"

The light in the kitchen at dusk was woolen and claustrophobic. I was out of cigarettes.

Penelope was chopping carrots and apples for the girls, a knife in each hand. She did not look up.

"When will you be back?"

"I'll be back for dinner, okay?" I stared at the flash of the knives. The snick and tock (tock) of them. (tock) I remember hearing both of the girls start to cry in the other room. (tock) I remember remembering that my wife was, in fact, a hypnotist, and I turned, and I left, and to tell you the truth one thing after another did not happen; I ate dinner in a diner and I slept in my office and spent the next morning at the University library reading literary magazines looking for ideas and then I faked my way through an afternoon workshop and I drove home, nauseous and anxious.

But that was the last day I remember well. I can not tell you anymore right now.

EXERCISES

1 Get some scissors and cut out a single line of dialogue from each comic strip on the comics page of your local paper. Put them into a hat and draw them out randomly. Arrange these into a conversation, then build a story around that conversation.

2 Take a tape recorder, and go to a fast food restaurant, and sit near a table of teenaged girls, and tape record their conversation. This will not probably help you write dialogue but it will show you how frightening and cutthroat the world of teenaged girls is.

3 No, wait, it will help. Take the tape, and play it backwards. What secret messages are embedded in their conversation? Write those messages out and use them as dialogue in your next story.

4 Walk around saying your dialogue, complete with tags, in everyday conversation, to test its effectiveness. Example: Walk into a convenience store and say, "'I would like to buy a pack of Marlboro's, please,' he said." Example: Walk into the local library and tap the shoulder of the old man who is dozing in the magazine section and say to him, "'Not on my beat, you don't,' he snarled." Take notes on the results.

5 Walk around saying the dialogue of other writers. EXAMPLES: "'Isn't it pretty to think so?'" "'You want my life? You need it? Here.'" "'That was my Lo, and these are my lilies.'" I don't know what this will accomplish. But you will be doing something with dialogue, anyhow, and that's got to be a step in the right direction, my beautiful readers.

CHAPTER TWELVE:
COMPLICATION

This is the chapter on complication.

The novice writer will be tempted to resolve the main conflicts of a piece too quickly. Once said conflicts are established, it is difficult to resist the temptation to bring everything to a head. It's like having the world's biggest secret and three drinks in you—you want to *tell!* Dear reader, oh my reader, just don't. You'll never forgive yourself in the morning.

As example, purely instructive:

But from that day forward, she keeps her best tricks to herself, and he does not ask to see them, ever.

He wishes he could talk about it, could clear the air. He feels this most often as the evening grows late, as they both emerge from their workrooms, smile, kiss each other fondly, turn on the television maybe for the late news, think about bed. Thinking about bed, he thinks about touching her in the dark, about whispering something sweet and restorative in her ear. But what he has not said about that day seems to block all that he would say in the future. And but yet again, every time he thinks about bringing it up, that sudden weightless flip of the stomach takes him, and he opens a beer or pours a drink instead. And he stays up until he's sure she's asleep, until he's had three or four or five drinks and will slide into bed and the safety of sleep simultaneously.

This is all interior, and prelude.

They moved to a house in the country and began to remodel, and here for a time he could further distance himself by floors and rooms and filling that space with students and ex-students and writers of note and un-note and lazy summer parties and long fall days and hushed hot spring mornings drinking screwdrivers out on the porch, his feet up on the railing. And/or afternoons ripping out walls and plastering and rewiring and painting and drilling sawing hammering buzzing banging cacophonous conversation-killing productivity. And she his perfect wife all alchemical in her secret basement workshops, obscuring and revealing, directing explosions, working with her nimble fingers and hands to bend what was, elevate it, transform it. He imagined her surrounded by workbenches spilling over with props: top hats and scarves and rabbits and hoops and rings and cigarettes and playing cards and doves and tigers and cages and shackles and flowers and guillotines and dribble glasses and whoopie cushions and wine glasses. Water to wine. Elixirs of love. Preparing illusions. This one's head, this one's body. Tricks.

And one spring morning she performed the first part of her greatest trick, and transformed her body. Of course, with the help of a volunteer from the audience. She came out and distracted him with a flash of cleavage and a swish of her robe and enchanted him and led him onstage and then everything was transformative. This one's head, this one's body. She brought him to her and him to her and together they changed her, utterly.

"Presto," she whispers into his ear as he enters her.

Outside he hears the footsteps of Andrew Shay slowly drifting past.

"Change-o," she gasps a little while later.

And, still later (say, nine and a half months), she is changed again, divides herself. "Nothing up my sleeve," he imagines she said at the moment of revelation, the moment she brings Chloe into the world.

But he wasn't there. He'll never know.

For eight months you planned to be there, or at least you said you wanted to be, and you sounded like you meant it. This was her longest and best trick. It worked. It had you both together, closer than you had ever been. You painted the nursery and shopped for rockers and read all the books together, cover to cover. You emptied your house of writers and wannabes and filled it to the rafters with toys and conversation. When she hooked herself up to the monitors and did the monthly ultrasound act, you swooned and applauded. You were back there for the long haul again, or so you said. You didn't care if you weren't writing, if the publications were trickling away, if you hadn't given a reading in months. You had everything you needed in that farmhouse. You sure sounded sincere.

So who can explain why, when Andrew Shay called and told you that the University of the Gulf needed a last-minute replacement reading just two weeks before the baby was due, you agreed?

"We could use the money," you said.

Do you remember the look in her eyes?

She let you go, though. The due date was two weeks away. You had plenty of time. You could use the extra money.

And the crowd was sparse and the air-conditioning broken and the reception chips and beer and a few drunk graduate students and too-loud music and you wanted to call her from there but the music was too loud to even hear a dial tone and you couldn't get a ride back to your motel so you finally walked, maybe a little drunk, five miles in night air like a swamp and you were so gone when you finally got there that you didn't even notice the little red light on the phone blinking.

At least her parents had been there to help out. At least Andrew Shay had been in town (he had been on his way down to hear your reading, but his car had had a flat, and he'd called and Penelope's water had just broken, and he drove to your house on three tires and a rim and rushed her to the hospital and was there for the delivery and what a good story it was later, except for the part about you not being there, of course) to lend a shoulder to cry on. At least you were there the next day, at least you cried when you held your daughter, at least you were a doting father, at least you realized how enormously you had fucked up. At least you wanted to atone.

There was, as she recovered and her parents and Shay hovered, an uneasy détente. She doled out easy forgiveness as she held Chloe to her breast, as her father clattered in the kitchen, perpetually doing dishes, as Shay appeared in the doorway, a glass of decaf tea steaming, always the right beverage and the right murmured words, as her mother gave new meaning to the word monosyllabic when she was around me (decidedly mixed emotions therefore ensued). And Penelope watched me, weak and woozy, as I changed my first diaper and rocked Chloe to sleep. When Chloe would awaken screaming in the middle of the night there was sometimes a weird fatigued traffic jam at her bassinet as I would leap to get her and Shay would stumble in on instinct (though he was an only child, so what instinct it was is mysterious) from my study where he slept with a pillow and a blanket on the floor, and her mother who would stumble in late from the living room sleeper sofa where her husband snored on, all of us reaching in to pick the baby up and give her to Penelope, pale and beatific in our bed. In these moments the tension eased somewhat and I could almost have wept for gladness, and I swore, later, as the moon shone pale blue on the blasted winter Alabama fields, that I would never screw up again, that I would always always always be there. But I could not somehow say this.

Instead I tried to write it, and often did, little notes or typed letters, dozens of drafts that I left out for her. I would leave them on the kitchen table, in creamy envelopes addressed to her, or on her pillow when she was in the bathroom, or in the bathroom when she was nursing Chloe. Many times I wrote my promises to her, in language achingly beautiful, the most gorgeous prose I have ever written. And the envelopes would disappear, and she would later smile a weary smile, but she would not speak a reply, nor write one. And the house would fill up with the clatter of cleaning and dishes washed and toilets scrubbed as Andrew Shay and her father and her mother busied themselves and tidied and tucked and scrubbed and boiled and rinsed and dried in the bathroom in the kitchen in the nursery in my study, it was as if my words and my resolve and my good intentions were dried and powdered and dusted away, and what was left between Penelope and I was sterile and gleaming long after everyone left us finally alone, a family.

You might wonder why Shay was still there, but that is the kind of student, the kind of man, he was. Sometimes, seeing him with Penelope then, I could almost see a whole other person in him, the man he would grow up to become, the splendidly intuitive writer. I know it seems like another person in the house then would only add to the complications. Somehow, though, he kept everyone happy. He had that knack for seeing what people needed. I was glad he was there. I never thought twice about it.

I looked, sometimes, for the notes I'd sent her. Drunk, I rifled her shoeboxes full of letters, but never found anything. The only letters she kept from anyone were written in foreign languages or invisible ink—I did not speak the language. I could not crack the code. But that was later. That was long after Miranda, our second child.

I wanted to have another child, and I wanted it fast, because I wanted to cement our family, because I wanted desperately to be a good man again, to be a loving husband, to be a family man. I thought that she would be a chance for me to prove myself. And when our second daughter was born, I was there.

Miranda was so beautiful as a baby, is so beautiful now, as is her sister Chloe. I wake up in the night sweating to think that I will not ever see them again. My Muse stares at me, perched on the baseboard, her night-seeing eyes huge in the darkness. She shakes herself and sighs. Outside the neon moon blinks restlessly.

I digress.

For a while, I was a wonderful father. I was. I did all of the right things. I loved and love my children. I loved and still love their mother. We were happy. I really think we were.

I digress.

We weren't at all.

I can't begin to tell it. We were good parents. We were, but we were strangers to each other. It could never go on like that. And in my despair as I saw that, I became hazardous. I wanted so much to be good. To have a family. To belong.

I can not tell you in words how it went wrong. It's not as if there was one unambiguous moment when we knew. I still think sometimes that it was a matter of fractions, of infinitely small moments, the shavings of errors that accumulated almost unnoticeably until the scale sighed downward and bumped, and bumped again. This is how complication works. The novice writer believes in obvious and immediate cause and effect, the story as fistfight, punch thrown and nose bloodied. The experienced writer knows that plot works by accrual, the slow accumulation of increasingly dreadful moments.

I can not bear to tell you any more.

This is the chapter on complication.

EXERCISES

I

CHAPTER THIRTEEN:
HOW TO WRITE LIKE
A MORNING IS

There is in the world so much that is luminously beautiful and words are hopelessly inadequate tools to use to try
to capture that beauty. Style, then, is a way for writers to try
to hide their inadequacies.

In the way that good tailors can disguise all kinds of
physical imperfections, think of your prose style as a suit of
clothing—will you walk down the street wearing a suit of
armor? A raccoon coat and blue jeans and sneakers? A
seersucker suit? A Joker tee shirt and khaki-esque shorts
and white socks scrunched down and high-top sneakers?
Will your prose be evening wear or garden wear?
Crotchless leather panties or lacy white frilly undies? Black
tie or seventies bellbottoms and polka-dotted muscle-
shirts? Some styles will make the mind's gorge rise, and
some styles will make the imagination swoon.

The above might suggest that there are an infinite variety of prose styles, and there are, and many of them are

good. Hemingway with his short declarative sentences and neutral diction (a dark suit with a crisp white shirt) is very different from Faulkner, with his lyrical, cadenced, very long sentences (sweeping battered trenchcoat over richly textured bright blue shirt, gleaming silver belt buckle buckling liquid silver pants). Is one better than the other? Is an apple better than an orange? You see, of course, that style is also all about taste, and tastes vary. I prefer apples and Faulkner. Penelope preferred strawberries and cream and Jane Austen. Her tastes may have changed. I'm not sure. (See Chapter XX: Mixing Metaphors.)

So, anyhow, taste is arbitrary and one thing is not better than the other and the house of fiction like the house of the Lord has many rooms and all that jazz. But how does that help you, you writers of the future? How can you forge a prose style that will ensure success?

Contrary to what the writers of other self-help books might tell you, there are seven unbreakable rules that one should follow to write prose that moves beyond the merely serviceable (I mean, anyone can move a plot along—it's just one word after another, like a guided museum tour, move along now, don't linger, hurry up to the next scene, the next plot point, hustle hustle hustle, to the left if you look closely you can see a strand of sub-plot, to your right a major complication and up ahead there is an ironic reversal, no lolly-gagging, and you there in the back, no photographs please. Don't we want more from our words? Don't we, dear readers, just want more of everything?). I digress. Seven rules. And I will tell them to you now.

1 Use only one adjective per sentence. Avoid adverbs.

2 Whenever possible, use colors in your description. Always refer to simple colors that everyone can picture. Don't say magenta, say red. Who knows what chartreuse or puce is? Words like that not only frustrate your readers, who can't picture any color at all, they're faintly gross sounding. Vermilion, teal, ochre. Don't you feel faintly sickened?

3 In every paragraph, use the same ratio of simple to compound sentences. It doesn't matter whether you use more simple or more compound sentences in a given paragraph, but each paragraph should be balanced similarly. For example, make sure that every paragraph of a story is composed of 22% simple sentences and 78% compound sentences. Try not to use compound-complex sentences. They're pretentious, disturbingly so, and they throw the formula off—we're writers, not mathematicians, right, reader?

4 Do refer to sounds, but do *not* refer to smells. Smells are mostly unpleasant. You may be tempted to throw bacon smells into a scene, or perfume, but don't—bacon is associated with grease and we all know how awful too much perfume can be. Every reader will always have some negative association with a smell. In fact, I would go so far as to say that all mentions of smell inevitably lead the reader to call up the smell of a fart. Bacon, for instance, almost always leads me to some gastric distress, and before you know it, I'm not thinking about that wonderful kitchen scene you

tried to evoke, I'm remembering the last time I was almost doubled over on the toilet. Or perfume—a woman's perfume often reminds me inevitably of sex, and as I call up different sexual moments I find myself remembering one awful tryst with the UFO Girl where I passed gas at the climactic moment and she thought it was an alien paralysis ray and scrabbled out from beneath me screaming, her nails raking my flesh, our (mostly my) bodily fluids spattering obscenely through the air. Suddenly, I am taken out of the scene. Sounds are very neutral, and can therefore be used by the skillful writer. Smells are never neutral. Never forget this.

(Note to self: is this really good advice? Check this tomorrow morning first thing. If the Muse won't help, ask Natasha the maid or what's-his-name the desk clerk. Don't forget.)

5 Use the same number of syllables in every paragraph, though you need not do so in every sentence. People crave order. Readers crave balance. Writers need structure. See Rule 3.

6 Contradict yourself. Confuse your descriptions. Never let a description do just one thing. Always leave one detail out of place. If you are clear and logical, your readers will have nothing to do, and will feel shut out, like they haven't really bitten into a whole apple or orange but only been handed a tiny slice (see Chapter XX: Extending a Metaphor). The more your reader puzzles over the psychic dissonance such strategies will provoke, the more they'll think

you've caught the whole of what you're describing. I think always of my favorite song here, "Oh, Susannah," and its contradictory lyrics: "It rained all night, the day I left / The weather it was dry. / When the sun came out, I froze to death. / Susannah don't you cry." No, it doesn't make sense; it is nigh unto nonsensical and yet it captures the tragedy of their relationship I think more completely than a more straightforward set of images might. Not what that relationship seems to be, but what it is.

Here is another example:

Absence is presence.

Another:

Nothing is something.

7 Use fancy poetic devices. Use a touch of synecdoche, layer every other sentence with alliteration, employ synesthesia, pepper each page with anaphora. The busier you are with poetic devices, the more you create the illusion of complexity that sometimes can fool your reader into thinking that you have caught, in mere words, the magic fabric of what *is.*

Let me give you an example:

That morning was cool. There was a breeze, and my windchimes tinged sweetly. The grass was fresh mown. It was green, and clumps of it were scattered about. My wife came out in her nightgown. She bent to kiss me, and exposed her exquisite cleavage to the world. There was a breeze. The morning was cool, and the grass murmured lullabies, freshly mown. The boy sitting next to me cleared his throat. The sound of it broke our mesmeric mouth-pleasures and she went inside. I followed her. Inside it was cooler, though there was no breeze. After a while he went away.

You may attempt to abandon the techniques employed above, and many writers have tried, but then you will not be writing like me, and will never achieve my success, which may actually be a blessing. I don't know what I meant by that. At night I sometimes open the curtains of my motel room and stare up not at the moon but at the huge neon crescent moon head of the Moon Winx Motel. He is a brilliant yellow, and wears a red sleeping cap, and does in fact wink his neon wink relentlessly. He smiles. Cruelly, I think, but perhaps just vapidly, and somewhere behind him I think is the real moon but I have not quite yet figured out what direction I am facing and my Muse is no help here, shrugging her angular shoulders, staring up raptly at the neon moon until I close the heavy curtains and she sighs and I crank the air-conditioning up to eleven and she returns to Hugo's *The Triggering Town* with a yellow highlighter and I return to the computer, and a vodka-and-tonic on the mouse pad, and you, darling readers.

EXERCISES

1 Write a page as if you were Hemingway the day after the first time he ever dropped acid. Write a page as if you were Hemingway the day before he committed suicide. Write a page as if you were Hemingway the same day he first made love with a woman.

2 Write a page as if you were Faulkner pretending to be Hemingway writing on the same day he first made love with a woman.

3 Write a page as if you were Jean Toomer or Virginia Woolf or James Joyce or Gertrude Stein, pissed off about never being mentioned in a chapter about style.

4 Devise a formula for paragraphs like this: Simple + Compound + Simple + Compound-Complex + Complex + Complex. Write every paragraph of a ten-page story following this formula.

5 Write a paragraph as if you were an ant crawling up a tree with a tiny bit of leaf in your mouth. As the ant is struggling, employ the most lushly lyrical prose style possible. Then write the same paragraph as if you were the same ant, this time crawling *down* the tree. As the ant will be cruising, use the tersest prose style imaginable. Remember: incongruity is your friend, the scary friend who drops by at seven in the morning while you are cooking bacon, or at ten-thirty just as you are taking the dog out for the last walk of the night.

6 Write a paragraph using as few words as possible. Now write a paragraph using as many words as possible. Now write one somewhere in between. Realize that most of your paragraphs will be in-betweeners. Try not to despair.

Now that you know *how* to describe, you might rightly wonder *what best* to describe? What is essential to the success of every story that must be painted in word-pictures?

Below is a list that I think you might find helpful—my dear good friend John L'Heureux made a photocopy of this list and gave it to Andre Dubus who passed it on to Jane Smiley and Tobias Wolff, who passed it on to Robert Stone and Richard Ford and John Edgar Wideman and Carolyn Alessio and Gordon Lish and Deborah Eisenberg and Steven Millhauser and Siri Hustvedt and A.M. Homes and Tom Canty and Julian Barnes and Floyd Skloot and so on and so on. The next time you read any of their stories, pay attention—you will see that they describe all of the items on said list below religiously. They are writers of the future!

Ten Things To Describe

I CHICKENS

This may seem like an odd animal to have to describe in every story, but it's imperative that you do. What characters do and say to chickens is a crucial key to "who they are," and if your readers are going to become engaged in that moment, they need to *see* that chicken. Is it healthy? Bedraggled? Fluff-puffy? Red? White? Brown? All of those colors? It is not the wheelbarrow that matters, but the chickens.

On the last day that I saw my daughters in our home, the morning of the day I went to the twenty-four-hour store for what turned out to be forty-eight hours, a parade of chickens wandered through the sun-bleached fields surrounding our house. I awoke on the couch, drenched with sweat, at some indeterminate early-morning hour, still in my clothes from the night before, still reeking of smoke and screwdrivers. I woke up knowing I had ten cigarettes left. I did not light one. I did not want to leave the house. The windows were all thrown open, the curtains perfectly still in the no-breeze. And then as the day cracked open sweating and feverish I heard the sound of a crow whose heart wasn't in it, a heat-wilted caw. And then the huffing and rustling and buck-badawing of many chickens, faintly at first, then louder and louder. I sat up; my mouth felt broken and my hands trembled. Chloe crept into the room, scared and cautious. She crawled into my lap and I stroked her hair.

"Daddy," she whispered, "what is it?"

"I don't know," I said, and I picked her up and she twined her hands in my too-long hair and buried her face in my shoulder and we went to the nearest window and looked out.

A rooster wandered as if dazed through our dusty yard, past the swingsets and baby pools. A line of chickens, red and brown and white, followed, spastically. It was a long line. It took at least five minutes for them all to pass through the yard and down the driveway and out of sight. Chloe would glance out the window, then hide her face in my shoulder and murmur.

"Daddy," she said, "I'm scared."

"Me too, sugar," I said. A sour smell hovered over or in me. I was afraid I would taint her with it.

"Daddy," she said, "where are they going?"

"I don't know, sugar."

"Daddy," she said as the last chickens wandered by. "What will happen to us?"

"I don't know, sugar," I said, one last time, watching the last small white chicken scurry past anxiously, already almost lost. By the end of the driveway it would be alone.

That was the last real conversation Chloe and I had without the word "visitation" lying thick and furry on the back of my tongue.

You may have some difficulty figuring out how to get a chicken into your story about urban angst or ten people in a lifeboat, but know that every piece of literature of note in contemporary fiction, from *The Adventures of Huckleberry*

Finn to *As I Lay Dying* to *Invisible Man* to *Ragtime* makes mention of a chicken. Reader, dare you not follow suit?

2 DOGS

We describe dogs because in doing so we are describing ourselves. Their eyebrows and their tongues and their fur and their skins—dogs are mirrors of the self held up to the self. Every beautiful story describes a dog. The dog that I had as a child was lovely, noble, telepathic, and had a vision about the moment of its death (too horrible for me to describe) many months before it happened, yet still went on bravely fetching sticks and chasing squirrels and thumping his leg when I scratched his sweet spot. Only later, after I saw him die, did I know he had been trying to tell me that death was near, that we should cherish our time together, that we should not squander a moment. It seems that the ones I love often attempt to communicate this very message. It seems that even now I am at best a retrospective communicator.

Some dark nights I could just weep.

3 EYEBROWS

It is eyebrows, not eyes, which are the windows to the soul, or perhaps the caterpillars of the soul, depending on the eyebrow, of course (see Chapter XX: Extending a Metaphor). In any case, spend less time describing hands and eyes and noses and mouths and hair and more time describing eyebrows. Your readers will thank you.

4 SHOWER CURTAINS

What a character has chosen for his or her shower curtain will say a lot about him or her. Is it a plain blue shower curtain? Transparent? Is it a Mickey Mouse or a Winnie the Pooh shower curtain? Does it have abstract geometric designs on it? And what condition is it in? Spotless? Creased with mildew? The few dismal nights I spent in the UFO Girl's one-bedroom apartment I was surprised to see that her shower curtain was elaborately pink and ruffled and spotless. The ones I had with Penelope were dark blue and opaque: though I heard her humming and the water beating, I could not see even her silhouette, I could not truly know it was her—it could have been anyone—until I pulled back the curtain and stepped inside with her, the steam swirling around us, her radiant rosy flesh meeting mine, relief and gratitude hard upon me. You describe a person's shower curtain and you have given me a gloriously true glimpse of their inner self.

5 THE TASTE OF HOT TEA WITH LEMON & HONEY IN IT

You may think that there would be limits to the ways you describe a cup of tea, and there are, but this is like jazz improvisation—the basic melody might stay the same, but the variations on the melody are where it's at. The tea melody is a staple of modern fiction (the ancients described mulled wine), and is a way for other writers to check each other out, and a way for the savvy reader to fix the writer's larger concerns. Thankfully for me, Penelope was a tea aficionado, and thought of it as an aphrodisiac, and helped me to understand the depth and complexity of hot tea with honey, and lemon, in a way that skyrocketed my career. The "hot tea description" is one of the best-kept secrets in the current literary scene. Only I would reveal it to you, oh my darling readers.

6 DEFECATION / URINATION

It was Martin Amis who clued me in to this one, and it was one of the best pieces of advice I ever got. All works of fiction must describe some form of bodily evacuation. Failure to do so will instantly brand you as pedestrian, if not downright Victorian. It is also, again, a useful way to convey character information to the reader. Does he hold his penis with one hand or two as he stands at the urinal? Does she dab or wipe? Does he or she clutch the underside of the toilet seat as he or she strains to defecate? Humanity is in these details! Humanity!

7 THE SMELL OF A CIGARETTE BEING LIT FROM THE WRONG END

Here's another humanity gauge, readers. I put a moment like this in every story, no matter who the characters are or what the time period is. Indeed, even considering the description of that moment and the ways that it varies when it involves an eleven-year-old and her first cigarette versus, say, a drunken frat boy playing a drinking game, is a consideration that always keeps my head fresh. Nine cigarettes into my last real day as a husband and just before dinner I lit the tenth and last from the wrong end, inhaled, gagged, and ground it out angrily. This was out on the front porch—I would not smoke around the girls as a general rule. I stared out at the listless fields and down our impossibly long driveway and I wondered what it would be like to quit, to never smoke again. But I could not let that taste in my mouth be my last taste of cigarette, and I rose, and I went inside, past Chloe and Miranda building with DUPLO blocks in front of the television (on *Sesame Street* Grover sang: "It rained all day, the day I left / The weather it was dry") and out to the kitchen and there I said, "I'm going to the store. Do you need anything?" and then eventually out the back door and into the Toyota and down the driveway, dust lifting behind me, the sun dropping suddenly as if shot out of the sky.

8 THE SOUND OF PAPER CRUMPLING

You might think that this was a sound that would only pop up in stories about writers or writing, but *au contraire, mon freck!* This sound speaks to something primal to us. Even before there was paper, in paperless cultures, oral traditions contain moments that describe this sound. It is an essential literary moment. I have printed out whole chapters of this book just to crumple them up and throw them into the trash before I deleted the files. I have filled baby pools with crumpled paper through which my Muse splashes happily, leaping and diving, her pale skin lost in the paleness of paper, her black bikini as if made of ink.

My last Muse, the Muse that finally came into my life when Penelope did, her skin was unsmudged. I was working on *A Banjo on My Knee* and I wanted to bronze every word. I wanted to put plastic over every single chapter as soon as I saved and titled it. And that Muse brought me coffee and purred and hummed and tidied up my desk and dusted the curtains and stroked the hair away from my forehead. I felt so normal I started to smoke a pipe and jog every afternoon after the day's writing was done, my Muse drifting along glistening in the heat, an unbreakable iridescent soap-bubble of a Muse.

I should have crumpled more paper.

9 THE WAY YOUR EARS POP ON AN AIRPLANE IF YOU HOLD YOUR NOSE AND CLOSE YOUR MOUTH AND BLOW VERY GENTLY

I have difficulty describing this moment, and it is sometimes a drag to trundle all of my characters up and put them on planes and make them pop their ears (and it was even more of a difficulty for pre-airplane-writers), but I know that the challenge elevates me as a writer. And it does always force my characters to keep moving which, in the fiction of the future, will be a definite advantage. I think of Andrew Shay as I write this, cool and collected, his blond eyebrows thick and well-tended and arched wryly as he strides through the airports, an old hand at this now, the Writer of the Future, jetting to readings and lectures and benefits and PEN meetings and AWP sessions, all the geek and gawk trained out of him, his walk loose and confident, his stomach flat, his sunglasses dark over his blue blue eyes, his white suit crisp, his purple shirt lint free, his hair well plugged, his teeth painfully white, his breath minty fresh, his very being a magnet for admiring glances, inner swoons and sighs. And I say, bravo, Andrew, keep moving, bravo. You are the Writer of the Future. I don't know that we'll ever catch up.

10 THE MOMENT YOU SAW YOUR CHILDREN AGAIN AFTER THEIR MOTHER LEFT YOU AND TOOK THEM AND RIGHTLY SO, FOR YOU HAD SO LOST YOUR WAY WITH HER AND NEITHER OF YOU WANTED THE GIRLS TO SEE YOU LIKE THAT OR TO GROW UP IN A HOUSE LIKE THAT AND GOD STILL IT HURT SO MUCH IT HURT SO MUCH THAT YOU COULD SCARCELY MAINTAIN ANY SEMBLENCE OF NORMALITY AS YOU TOOK THEM TO MCDONALD'S AND HUGGED THEM AND WAITED WITH THEM ALL DAY TO GET THE NEXT WAVE OF BEANIE BABIES AND THE NEXT AND THE NEXT AND STILL YOU MISSED BERRY BEAR AND YOUR YOUNGEST CRIED AND YOU CRIED AND AFTER THAT YOU CHECKED INTO THE MOON WINX MOTEL AND DID NOT SEE THE GIRLS THE NEXT WEEK OR THE WEEK AFTER OR THE WEEK AFTER BUT THEN YOU DID THE FOLLOWING WEEK AND IT WAS CHUCK E. CHEESE AND IT WAS A DISASTER AND IT ALL ENDED IN TEARS AGAIN AND YOU COULDN'T STAND TO GO THROUGH IT AGAIN BUT YOU DID AND GOD REALLY NEITHER COULD THEY BUT THEY DID, HOPING YOU JUST FIGURED OUT WHAT THE HELL WAS WRONG WITH YOU OH WHERE DID IT ALL GO WRONG?

EXERCISES

1 Describe an egg. Do not use any adjectives or adverbs.

2 Describe your left knee. Now describe your left knee as if you were a paranoid schizophrenic. Now describe your left knee as if you were three years old. Now describe your knee as if you were eighty-three, and in the first stages of Alzheimer's. (See also: Chapter Eighteen Points of View)

3 Describe a cathedral. Appeal to all five senses. Describe a grain of salt. Appeal to all five senses.

4 Describe the way you felt the morning after the first night that you made love, the way she slept curled into you, the way the wet spot still lingered somewhere near your rump, the way the sunlight fell across your feet, and your toenails needed cutting, and the stack of books beside her bed smelled slightly mildewed, and you needed to pee, but didn't want to wake her, and didn't want to encounter her roommate whom you heard stirring just twenty minutes ago, and how lovely her hair smelled. Describe that as if you were never going to forget it, as if it would sustain you through the difficult times. Describe it so that it will be an image that will save your marriage.

5 Describe the worst day of your life without ever mentioning what made it so awful. Do not use the word "feel" or "sunlight" or "dark" or "tears." Do not mention any part of your body, and do not bring up doors, cars, beds, or animals.

6 Describe the rest of this page. Do not use any metaphors. Do not use the words "blank" or "white" or "empty" or "sad."

CHAPTER FIFTEEN:
THE OBLIGATORY
SEX SCENE

There will come a time, sweet reader, when you will perhaps need, for important plot or character reasons, to describe your characters making love.

Sex can be a daunting task for most writers.

Nevertheless, that shouldn't stop you from writing a sex scene.

If you find yourself suffering from a relative poverty of images to draw upon from your own experience, I strongly suggest that you imagine your friends in bed. While this might ordinarily be a distasteful or even unhealthy occupation, remember that you are a writer! This is necessary for your art. Imagine such scenes in great detail. What does each party look like nude? Can you picture their sexual organs? What positions do they favor? Do they indulge in any sort of kinkiness? Out and out perversion? Try to imagine different friends with different partners. Or, imagine them in threesomes, or indulging in group sex. Who would do what, to whom? For how long? What sounds would they make?

Keep in mind that you are doing this for art's sake.

Once you've imagined such scenes, it's a simple matter to describe them. Still, beginners may want further advice. Here are some rules I try to follow when I'm crafting a sex scene:

1 Always try to use the word "sex," to show your readers that you are describing this on purpose, and that you have a higher purpose, namely the artistic integrity of your work. You can use the word as a verb ("'Shall we sex now?' she said nonchalantly.") or as a noun ("Then he gazed lovingly upon the sex of his lover.").

2 Use as many euphemisms as possible. This will make you seem less like a pornographer and more like an artist, in case you were worried about such a distinction. A vagina is a "teapot of love." Making love is the "tempest in a teapot." An erect penis is a "flesh flagpole" (thus ejaculation is "raising the flag"). "The bruised plum." "The inbox of passion." "The satellite dish." "The trash compactor." Need I go on?

3 Use food and toys. Most people are tired of the same old boring sex scene: she spreads her legs charmingly, he enters her, they sweat and whisper and move around athletically, things reach their climax, or not, as the case may be. Boring. Next time, put a can of whipped cream under the bed or a cucumber in the bedside drawer. Hide an inflatable Betty Boop doll in the closet, or tuck a vibrator called the Silver Bullet under the mattress. Remember,

you're the writer! If you want an enema bag in the scene, make sure your character just happens to have a spare in his or her suitcase!

4 Make sure your scene is always about something else. A sex scene should not just be about sex, but about character, or politics, or art. That couple in the next room at the Moon Winx Motel making love so hard they rattle the pictures off the wall could be used in a story to make a point about politics—she's a poor liberal, and he's a rich conservative (or vice versa). Instant symbolism! (And the poor guy in Room 6 who has not had sex since that quickie in the back yard of the reading party four months ago, he voted for Nader last election.) The white Manhattanite couple that spray paint "gang" graffiti on each other is not just an interesting diversion in the contemporary novel, they are a political-artistic statement.

On a more basic level, the character who makes love tenderly reveals certain aspects of self. The character who makes love poorly reveals obvious defects of personality. The character who makes love inventively is obviously to be admired—for your reader, this fact is an instant insight into inner character.

Let me give you an example of a sex scene from my abandoned novel *A Banjo on My Knee*—the novel was terrible, of course, but this scene works, not just because it is arousing, but because it is so layered with meaning:

The late afternoon sun oozed in the edges of the blue, recently-dusted curtains. The air conditioner raised the gooseflesh on our pale skin as we crouched on the bed like wiry love-starved animals.

"Darling," she said, holding the humming silver vibrator against her chocolate drop nipples, "now you will know what it is to engage in cultural discourse."

I snarled something appropriately postmodern. My pencil of lust was prepared to write voluminously on the subject. She waved the vibrator like a wand and the temperature dropped another ten degrees and the curtains opened and we imagined whole audiences from Wisconsin and Iowa sitting on hastily-erected bleachers gazing in transfixed, and then we lunged at each other in the sudden shock of sunlight that was like flowers bursting open behind our eyes.

To me, this is not just a funky hot sex scene, it also does much to tell us about these people—their shy newness with each other, their tender wounded childhoods are there if you read between the lines. And, on another level, it critiques post-Cold War politics and Internet-era exhibitionism. Bravo, I say, even if I did write it! That I burned the rest of the book has little to do with the success of that scene.

To summarize the nature of the sex scene and your role in its creation, I direct your attention to the following diagram.

When in doubt, insert Tab A into Slot B, or draw an arrow at random—you're bound to connect somehow.

(Note to Self: and if there is no diagram? What does the blank space become? Do I, alone in the darkness of the motel, imagine a diagram? Do I think of Penelope, diagramatically? Do I have to stir up enough energy to have an empty diagrammatical fantasy about Daisy the maid? If there's ever a reader for this, what will she or he see as he or she gazes at that shallow stretch of white? Is white space a nothingness to be filled? And what, then, does that make all of these fucking words?)

EXERCISES

1 Have a lot of sex. Write about it.

2 Do not have sex for thirteen months. Write about the different ways you imagine having sex.

3 Think of as many different phrases for male and female genitalia as you can. Use as many of these phrases as you can over the course of your sex scene. Some examples: the furry Wookie, the checkbook, the cream dispenser, the dub of love, the hollyhock, the seatback tray in an upright position.

CHAPTER SIXTEEN: NINE WAYS TO JUMP-START YOUR WRITING

There will come a time when you feel the itch to write like a rash creeping over your mind, but when you sit down to the typewriter or the computer, nothing happens. What follows are ten ways to get started when the spirit is willing but the imagination stammers.

1 WATCH TELEVISION

Don't just watch a little television, either. Watch hours and hours and hours of it, and all different kinds. I know that old famous dictum of Hemingway's (or was it Gordon Weaver's?), that you should write what you know, but really, who has time to know all there is to know? And who has the kind of life that could allow them to just get up and go to the Himalayas or down the Mississippi or the like? Television is a great big Technicolor window onto the world, and if you've seen it on television, you've experienced it, really, in a way, haven't you? Of course you have. If you've watched *NYPD Blue*, you know what it's like to be a detective in New York City. You know that police say things like "I'll keep a good thought out for you," or "I'll reach out to him." You know what police wear, and can write about it. As my dear tango partners Tom Rabbitt, John Keeble and Wright Morris might say, "You can write it if you see it!" Watch nature programs and *Sesame Street* and especially daytime talk shows—who knew there were so many people with so many sick thoughts, just like you? Before Jerry Springer and Rikki Lake and Geraldo Rivera and Oprah Winfrey, I thought I was alone in my aberrance. What a comfort television is, and what a source of material.

Here now in the Moon Winx I have a staticky television that I watch only sporadically. Maybe five-six hours a day. I don't think it's healthy to obsess over what is, essentially, just another writer's tool. Sometimes I find myself staring out at the yellow neon moon and drifting into reverie, as if each pulse was a plot point. Sometimes I stare at my computer monitor waiting for the 9:00 dramas to come on. All screens being equal, you know, all bright colors being compelling.

I used to wonder how novelists could ever finish a single book in the ages before television, but it has occurred to me that back then plays and puppet shows and operas and the like were sort of the same thing. Now, of course, plays are pretty highbrow, but back then people wrote plenty of trash just like you see on television. Fourteen-year-olds making a suicide pact? Angsty twenty-something kills stepfather and others in killing spree? Crazy woman kills children to get back at her recently remarried ex-husband? Tormented man kills father and marries his mother? Murder, incest, cannibalism, genocide, every week at the local theater. *Vive l'art!*

2 TAKE A WORKSHOP

The very best workshops to take are graduate level workshops, but they are difficult to get into, because you have faculty members who have sometimes quirky taste, and because they have all sorts of formal degree-related requirements. Fortunately, for purposes of inspiration, any writer's group will do.

Writer's groups or workshops are important because they allow you to be exposed to good ideas that you can use better, later. You'll have to change surface details, of course, to avoid the allegation of plagiarism. I have heard a rumor about *The Sun Also Rises*. You can see how a story about a fellow named Jake Barnes who'd had his testicles blown off in the war, and was still hopelessly in love with his ex-girlfriend but couldn't do anything about it anymore because, well, he'd basically been castrated, though the mechanics of that have never been quite clear to me, you can see how that is essentially the story of Nick Carraway, staring longingly at Jay Gatsby's green lights.

Remember, it's not plagiarism if you do it better.

3 EAT

Eating doesn't just nourish the body, it nourishes the mind, which is, of course, part of the body, so this should not come as a shock to anyone, really. If you want to burst with creativity, eat to excess. Some people think that fish is brain food—if you think so, too, then eat a fish an hour. Gorge yourself on shrimp, too, and clams and mussels and sushi.

You know the old saying "you are what you eat"? It's true! And the books that you write are, in part, what you eat too! Try eating nothing but lettuce for a week and see how it changes your prose. Adopt an all-chocolate diet if you would like your prose to be more lyrical (it's a little known fact that Faulkner did this). Just like a chicken diet made Wade Boggs a great hitter, the chicken diet will do wonders for your plots. Poets, eat grits and bacon to avoid sentimentality! The sophisticated novelist will experiment with his or her menu sometimes for years until he or she finds the perfect balance.

I have it on good authority that Ethan Canin eats Denny's Grand Slams three times a day while writing. My dear friend Melissa Hardy buys a bag of oranges and a cooked honey-glazed ham a week when she's working and drinks nothing but water. Some writers have varied diets, but eat a particular food daily no matter what else they eat: Graham Swift has crushed walnuts with every meal. George Garrett has one Pixie stick a day. Donna Tartt does eat a pastry a day, but avoids tarts. Tim O'Brien is partial to Fenway franks, but only when he's writing novels. I don't know what he prefers when he's writing short stories or nonfiction.

The key to this one is to gorge, especially as you just start out. The more you eat, the more you will be inspired. Watch the ideas explode out of you!

4 THROW A PARTY

Not only will you have fun and also make many people owe you favors (assuming you throw a good party), but you will get many ideas for stories and poems by watching your guests.

"But Gus," you say, "couldn't I just go to a party and avoid all of the trouble of throwing one?"

Yes, dear reader, but then you miss the opportunity to carefully control the parameters of your party environment. Let's say you want some ideas about human suffering. Serve chili and beer and coffee and then disable your toilet. Watch your guests' reactions carefully—especially facial expressions. If you need to take some notes about human passion, lace your drinks with Viagra and/or Ecstasy. You get the idea—what would you do at a party to inspire anger? Sadness? Get creative!

It is wise, by the way, if you want to be invited to other people's parties, that you not let your guests know about any of your manipulations. And when you go to the parties other writer's throw, always be prepared for their own hijinks. Whenever I go to Norman Mailer's place on the Cape, I always bring a Mason jar to pee in.

5 HOLD A BABY

There is something about holding a baby, especially a good baby, though a fussy one will do, that fills one with all sorts of profound and creative thoughts. The secret is to hold them until they fall asleep, their little snores a sweet inspirational music, their drool on one's shoulder the most vital kind of creative juice.

The tricky part is writing while you hold them. When my first girl Chloe was young, I used an architect's drafting board to write on. I'd raise it to a comfortable level and write long hand while I rocked her. She often needed to be walked and rocked, and on such occasions, I would write on a Post-it note I'd place on her forehead or bum, depending.

Hemingway not only wrote standing up, but with a baby in one arm. It took three babies for him to finish *Across the River and Into the Trees*.

If you have no babies of your own, you will have to place an ad and present yourself as a babysitter. You'll find no shortage of willing parents, and will make a little bit of money on the side, to pay for postage and the like. Hemingway was well known as a fine babysitter. His rates were reasonable, and he was a skilled diaper-changer and bath-giver. That he was able to write while changing diapers or giving baths is just further testimony to his genius.

Just now I had such an ache in my hands and arms, some lingering muscle-memory of Chloe and Miranda as I held and changed them. But that was long ago. That was long ago.

6 PIERCE SOMETHING

You would be surprised at how many famous writers are pierced, in places you might not have ever—or ever wanted—to imagine. I will whisper no whispers about Saul Bellow or Salman Rushdie, and you didn't hear it from me, capiche? You won't hear Russell Banks talking about this in any interview. But it's the rare writer who is not pierced somewhere, somehow.

The ritual of piercing, the planning of it, deciding on the piece of jewelry to first adorn the piercing, the careful cleansing necessary to avoid infection—this is all the ritual of writing, of planning, of conception, of care and nurturing. In both cases, the final product is something you carry with you for a very long time. Some books are right out there—ear or nose or tongue piercings—and some books are like secrets, are intimate revelations—the nipple or cock or clit or labia or anus piercing, for example. You and an elite few know all of the pleasures hidden away that you carry with you always.

Piercing is inspirational. Whenever I get stuck trying to think up my next project, I get in my Cadillac El Dorado and drive down to the Tattoo and Body Piercing Emporium at the local mall. The nipple rings in my left nipple (three of them) sparked my last collection of short stories. The tongue-stud was my fifth novel. And this book—well, three infections later, I've finally gotten used to and even enjoy the extra tug on a certain portion of my genitalia.

I don't trust the sincerity of writers who get tattooed (the self is not art, dear reader)—but I will go to hell and back with a writer who's been pierced.

7 PROSTITUTE YOURSELF

On the theory that one must experience new things, and that art requires sacrifice, I recommend all writers, male and female, prostitute themselves for a day. Wear your tightest clothing, and go to a borderline neighborhood, if there is one within driving distance, and walk suggestively. Most of us have seen enough television prostitutes to have a rough idea of what to do. If you're still not sure what to do, rent *Pretty Woman* or *Midnight Cowboy*.

If you don't live near a shady neighborhood, go to a sports bar and drink non-alcoholic beverages until someone approaches you for sex. You'll be surprised at how many people will pay you for it.

The experience will give you plenty to write about. You will know the feel of pavement and broken glass through the knees of your jeans. If you're lucky enough to be taken to hotels, you can also collect trial-sized shampoos and soaps. You may learn interesting facts about your friends and neighbors and political leaders. You will probably learn interesting facts about jail cells and courtrooms. Certainly it will prepare you for a Hollywood career. It will also earn you at least five dollars (it depends on you, and supply-side economics) that you can put towards postage and contest entry fees.

8 MASTURBATE

One reason to write is to explore your inner self, to give expression to that part of you that is not easily expressed. As within, so without. Most people do not spend enough time masturbating. They either make love or abstain. Either one is a mistake. Making love is not egocentric enough (unless you work hard only to please yourself, which I've heard is the truth for many men, but I digress), but abstention sublimates and frustrates energies that need to be released if one is to nurture one's creative side—this is the reason few good books are written by nuns and priests—if you happen across a good book written by a nun or priest, you can safely assume certain things about his or her night-time habits. Again, I digress.

When I am working on a book, I like to masturbate daily in a dark closet, sitting cross-legged on the floor, surrounded by shoes. It's important not to have a towel or Kleenex nearby, but to get in touch with those bodily fluids. Do, though, clean up somehow before you sit down to the keyboard again.

Um, I would add that this is a technique that I only use when I am working on fiction. No bodily fluids have been spilled in the writing of this book. That would be a terrible image for you to have lingering as you read, me sitting cross-legged on the floor of Room 6, the thin carpeting scratching my bony butt, the brisk knock at and the sound of keys rattling in the door as I leapt up scrabbling for a sheet and Delores the maid started to bustle in, daylight blustering, the acute embarrassment and stammered excuses coming from us both as I burrowed under the covers and she backed out blushing, the growing infrequency thereafter in which my room was actually, you know, cleaned. No, dear readers, focus instead on the art of fiction. Never forget the importance of words. Never lose sight of your love, your language.

I digress.

I used to write stories about people in cars.

I was proud of this, as I had created a genre, the "people in cars" genre. The genre had certain rules. The cars had to be in motion for at least a portion of the story. While occupants could exit or be ejected from the cars, no dramatic action would take place outside of the car's interior. A car would be defined as anything with four wheels.

After six years, two story collections (*People in Cars,* and *Different People in Different Cars*) and a novel (*I Brake for Small Animals*), I think I exhausted most of the possibilities of the genre. The point is that the rules of genre stimulated me for a long time, but I was not afraid to abandon genre when it was no longer productive. For a while I toyed with various sub-genres (people in airplanes, people in trains), but in the end they all seemed like dead ends.

It was my daughters who taught me how to discover my next genre.

I have for many years now been writing what my dear wonderful friend Milan Kundera once described as "Jonesian realism" (not to be confused with "Jonesin'"). That is to say, not quite realistic realism. For a while, I called it Midwest Grotesque in all of the interviews I did, but the name never stuck, and after a while the interviews stopped. Anyway, the point here is an examination of genre. Though I did wonder why the interviews stopped. Was I not witty enough? I was drinking a bit in those days, and doing the occasional line, so perhaps I was a bit loopy, though the interviews seem lucid and smart to me even now. Then, too, when things went wrong with Penelope, I got a little depressed, and stopped answering the phone and going out, so that might have had something to do with it. It could simply be that people got tired of me working the phrase "Midwest Grotesque" into every single response ("QUESTION: What do you typically have for breakfast? ANSWER: Well, before I sit down to a good, solid (or is that soiled, ha ha!) day of writing my Midwest Grotesque-ries, I like to eat a Red Baron Sausage or Bacon Breakfast Pizza, sometimes two. QUESTION: Who are you reading these days? ANSWER: Well, Flannery O'Connor, of course, whose use of the grotesque was an inspiration as I entered into what I now call my 'Midwest Grotesque' period." Gah! What was I thinking? (Always be humble, dear blessed reader.))

I digress.

In the fiction of the future, mere realism will not suffice, as life itself will be hyper-real. We must find a way to make our fiction amplify or even transcend the hyper-reality of reality—we should write hyper-hyper-realism, or non-hyper-realism. In other words, we should write Jonesian realism, which is all about being hyper and non-realistic, at both of which I excel, especially these days.

As I mentioned before, it was really my daughters who taught me how to write Jonesian realism. Chloe, then Miranda: both had such interesting responses to the world. Things that I took for granted—gravity, say, or rain—fascinated and perplexed them. The stories that they delighted in were outlandish and repetitive. The Spot videos that they watched were simple and oversized, full of bright colors and uncomplicated animation and awkward dubbing and a total disregard of the intricacies of plotting. And they wanted to watch them for hours and hours! Sitting on the couch one day next to Chloe (who was almost two-and-a-half) with Miranda (who was six months) bouncing sideways on my lap and drooling and reaching for my glasses, watching for the zillionth time as Spot and his friends Tom and Helen and Steve played in a park full of ominous white spaces and a lack of horizon, it hit me like a thunderbolt— why couldn't my fiction catch a little bit of what so delighted my daughters? I ducked my head from side to side and finally took off my glasses, and Miranda began to cry, and I barely heard her. Gradually, over the course of the next dozen stories, the rules of Jonesian Realism took shape.

In Jonesian realism, there are always dogs. They're not the focal point of each story, as they are in my lovely good friend Brad Watson's *The Last Days of the Dog-Men*. They're just there, because in the hyperreal world of the future, dogs will often be present. In my stories, they are *always* present. Amplitude.

In Jonesian realism, the laws of physics are mutable. Not to the degree that they are in cartoon physics, but still. If gravity needs to be an aggressive and singular force, as it was in *A Banjo on My Knee,* pulling the narrator down to his knees at the most inopportune moments, then gravity becomes just that fickle and malicious. If time needs to flow backwards for long or short stretches, then time shall operate like a VCR, with a Play button, a Fast-forward, a Rewind, a Pause, and even tracking adjustments if time gets too blurry or seems to be operating at a slightly different speed than is the reader, or time-speed in other books. It took my daughters forever to figure out time—yesterday and tomorrow and hour and minute were all the same to them, really, or confusingly similar. I wanted a fiction that operated on Toddler Time.

In Jonesian realism, one should always expect character or plot to be sacrificed for a really good description, a dazzling point of view trick, a verbal pyrotechnic, a good (or bad!) joke, anything that lets the authorial voice (okay, me) show off. This wouldn't work in a strictly realistic story, but in Jonesian realism, it can come off nicely. I will, for example, put men in gorilla suits for no other reason than that it tickles my funny bone. My daughters taught me the essential illogic of the world. And now I'm teaching you.

Jonesian realism must always, always avoid anything even remotely autobiographical. It's all well and good for some writers to make nice suits out of the fabric of their lives (see Chapter XX: "Extending a Metaphor). But my private life is my own business, and a shabby and ordinary thing besides. I may tap into things that I would regard as emotional truths, but I avoid talking about myself at all costs. Once, near the end, after we had made perfunctory love, Penelope said to me, "You never open up. You never let me in. You're like a magician who's all distraction and no revelation." When I did not say anything, she disappeared from the bed in a yellow cloud of disgust. What could I have said? She had been right, of course. My struggle for the right words—for any words—was not a failing but a— what is the word I'm looking for here? Not punishment. If I had loved her more truly, I would have found exactly the right words, whenever I needed them. So. Autobiography. Autobiography is for those without imagination. Or maybe those who can love wisely and well. I'm sorry to be the one to break it to you, my gentle ones.

These then, are the hallmarks of Jonesian realism, born on a couch by a man watching Spot videos with his daughters. (I miss you, Miranda and Chloe.)

Oh, the point: if you know the rules of the genre you want to write in, the rest is just filling in the blanks. I admit that the first novel I attempted in my new genre did not quite work out, but that was my fault for not focusing on the blanks. Or the filling. Or something.

My Muse looks at me somewhat betrayed. And of course, it's nice if you have a Muse as wonderful and gifted as mine, as devoted and tender and versatile as she surely is, to help ensure that what you fill in is something special. Somewhat mollified, my Muse returns to the pile of books and literary magazines she has open on the bed: Gass's *Fiction and the Figures of Life,* the *Gettysburg Review,* Behn and Twichell's *The Practice of Poetry, The Chariton Review,*

Burroway's *Writing Fiction, Crab Orchard Review,* Bugeja's *The Craft of Poetry,* Charles Baxter's *Burning Down the House,* Hirsch's *How to Read a Poem,* Chiarella's *Writing Dialogue,* Mock's *You Can Write Poetry, Black Warrior Review, New Orleans Review, The Southern Review,* Anne Lamott's *Bird by Bird, Agni,* tattered copies of *Movieline* and *Entertainment Weekly.* She covers herself in ink, massages it in deliberately, absorbs it through the flesh. She mewls and murmurs orgasmically. I look away, blushing.

So now I am authorized to say yes, readers, it is just that easy. Fill in the blanks. Don't turn on me now, oh my benign and beneficent readers! You're almost all I have left!

EXERCISES

1 Invent your own genre. Here are some examples:
  A People in Heaven stories
  B People Eating stories
  C The Arctic (similar to the Western, but colder)
  D Penguin stories

2 As John Gardner suggests in *The Art of Fiction*, combine genres. For example:
  A People Eating in Heaven stories
  B the Arctic grotesque
  C Penguin Horror stories
  D suburban fairy tales
  E Magical Automobile Realism

3 Try to describe your work like this: "It's a cross between _____ and _____ ." For example, "It's a cross between Kafka and Charles Chesnutt." Or, modify the statement a tad: "It's a cross between Toni Morrison and Stephen King, with just a touch of J.D. Salinger thrown in." A variation sentence that works well is "It's like _____ as written by _____ ." For example, "It's like *Hamlet* as written by Maya Angelou." Then go and write stories and novels that fit your description. Yes, it is just that easy. Trust me.

CHAPTER EIGHTEEN: POINTS OF VIEW

I t's not just that every story has two or two billion sides, it's that each of those two billion sides could be told in a variety of ways. How many permutations of this story can you come up with? A woman trips as she gets off a city bus and falls to the pavement. Do you tell it from the bus driver's perspective? Or another passenger's? Or all the passengers'? Or a bystander or many on the street? Or the pigeon she startled when her face slapped the pavement? Do you tell it from the woman's point of view? First, second, third limited, third dramatic or third omniscient? Past, past conditional, present, or future tense? The beginning writer might well be paralyzed by all of the choices afforded, but need not be.

Ask yourself this, dear reader: if my own life were a story, from how many points of view could it be told? That kid you made fun of in the third grade—imagine your life as told by him/her. The students whose names you've already forgotten—how would they tell your life? That dog you had as a child and loved who died so terribly and knew that death was impending when you didn't, though you should have, you could have done something if you had only known—how would that dead dog, frozen in mid-air, body half-turned to look back at you, tell your story? The woman who pulls you in to make love some sunny-ish morning, or the kid you leave on the porch, or you yourself—which version of that moment is true? If you put all three versions together, is it truer? This one's top, this one's bottom, and what in the middle? What about the child who was conceived at that moment? Do you tell your story from her point of view? The creak of the porchboards the sigh of the bedsprings the wash of fluids the sun the whisper the precise moment of leave-taking and of transformation—now who best to see and tell all of that?

I am thinking now, as I often do, of Shakespeare's *Othello,* and the way Shakespeare manipulates the audience's perceptions of events. We know from the very start of the play how breathtakingly wicked Iago really is, but the characters don't. To them, Iago is just another good ol' boy, "honest Iago." For them, the world unravels mysteriously—chaos without seeming cause. As if the world itself was profoundly disordered. Would it be a comfort, then, to know that your world was not chaotic, that your incredible sorrow was in fact authored by a single villain? And could a writer achieve the same effect in this day and age, when so many readers do believe in a disordered world? What if you had a book where the secret villain of the piece wrestled with conflicting desires: to get away with "it" (whatever "it" is; we're speaking hypothetically here, of course) and to boast about "it," to let his ego sing sing sing sing sing! Would you let your readers suspect this from the start? Would you let the characters? Would the revelations at the end be for the reader, or the characters, or both?

Who, in other words, is really telling this story?

It doesn't matter, dear reader, as long as somebody sees. As long as somebody sees the/a truth, however darkly, however fleetingly.

None of that even gets into point of view proper, as in pronouns and tenses and et cetera (see below).

Let me give you some handy tips that may help you make some basic decisions.

First, about tense:

Present tense is ideal for adding tension to a story—the outcome is always in doubt! Past tense is perfect for making readers happy and comfortable in a narrative. Future tense is wonderful if you want to lend a philosophical air to your words. So if I want to write a comforting tragedy, I write third person past tense ("He was not happy his line drive struck the child in the head and put her in a coma, but in the long run, he learned to live with it, and accept God's mysterious ways"). If I want to write an edgy humorous piece, I use first person present tense ("I am perplexed when I wake up next to the clown"). If I want to appear deep and complicated, I write in the second person future tense ("You will tumble into a pond with no bottom, and the giant carp will smell you in the water and rise, their dark jaws open").

As for pronouns:

In general, I use first person for happy stories and third person for sad stories. I use second person when I write tragi-comedies. Don't switch from one point of view to the other as it confuses readers about whether or not you are writing a comedy or a tragedy or what.

Point of view is really about WHO is calling the shots from WHERE, at WHAT DISTANCE! Consider all of your possibilities carefully!

Imagine *Moby Dick* written in the third person, or *As I Lay Dying* first person present tense Vardaman, or "Why I Live at the P.O." written in third person omniscient. I'm not saying that these very good writers made the wrong choices, but wow, just look at all of the possibilities out there!

My Muse is suddenly by my ear, whispering, her lips silky, her breath like clover and saltwater. "Let me give you an example," she whispers.

Let me give you an example:

On winter nights in Alabama when the wind snuck down their chimney and seeped through the panes, they would huddle together in blankets before the fire, and he would tell stories, and she would spin illusions, sometimes tossing a fine dust into the fire that would flare up in many colors, sometimes pulling scarves or gold pieces from someone's ear or mouth or nose. Their heads would be cold, and they could sometimes see their breath in the air, but underneath the blankets they would be warm and they would hold hands, and they would stare at the fire. And he would tell stories, about chipmunks in winter and crows that talked and bluebirds that wanted blueberries to break their enchanted state. The littlest daughter always fell asleep, awash in blankets and words and radiance, her cheeks red. She knew she would always be safe. She knew that this warmth of words, this wealth and treasure, would never not be a part of her world. The older daughter shifted uneasily between them. She dreaded the silence between the words, the darkness between flashes, the mutability of everything around them as it gave up gold or became something else. She would stare at the shadows in the corner, and she would feel her nose grow numb with cold, until her mother rubbed it, until her mother pulled a rabbit's foot from her left nostril. It was the flicker of light and shadow that hypnotized her into a sleep that was always flushed and worried. And cross-legged he sat and cross-legged she sat, knee touching knee, their children between them. And they would touch their children as a way to touch each other. And she would turn the fire green for them and the green flames would say, "Look, look, why can't you love me?" And he would say "Once upon a time" as if it meant "Please, let's start over." Warm and yet cold, almost together, they sat and held their children until the fire was embers and dawn was almost there, a fierce thing, roaring up from the east, sweeping across their lonely field.

"That's point of view," my Muse says. But I can not look at the computer screen just now.

And then I digress:

If you're bored with the same old same old, you should try to write in the fourth person.

In physics, the fourth dimension is time. Time, like gravity, is an unseeable but unbreakable fact of the universe. It only moves in one direction. It further pinpoints and limits a thing's existence. It is always there but never there, and that is what the fourth person in prose should be.

Here are the rules of fourth person:

1 The only pronoun you may use is "it."

2 Employ the objective omniscient.

3 Do not employ any chronological structure.

4 Use every tense in every sentence.

A brief example:

It carols; was stunned to learn of starvation, and will pass the hat upon completion of next to last hymn. Killed assembled with that last shot, its throat opens up; its crowd will scream hosannas. The backboard sighed apart, and checks will be cashed—it begins its downward arc, crowd ascendant, transported.

That was a paragraph about Reggie Miller hitting a last-second shot against the Knicks as told in fourth person.

In other words, if God was autistic and spoke to us, He'd speak in the fourth person.

EXERCISES

1 Pretend you are God (and not autistic). Write a story.

2 A man is falling off of a cliff. Write that story as if you were the man, in first person present tense. Write that story as if you were the cliff, second person, any tense. Write that story as if you were the air, in third person limited, past tense. Write the story as if you were the ground, in third person limited, present tense.

3 Rewrite "Why I Live at the P.O." in third person omniscient.

4 A man sits alone in a motel room and wonders how it all went wrong, how he wound up here, what the hell they're doing in the next room to make that disgusting noise, where that line of ants is going with the crumbs they are hauling away from his pizza boxes, how long it will take them to haul away every edible scrap, how long until his life will be stripped clean, whether he has enough booze to get through the night, whether he will wake up in the morning, whether he will finish his next book before he dies, what his children are doing right now, whether or not he'll sober up and straighten up enough to be a part of their lives again, whether anything will ever be right and good in the world ever again. Write that story as if it was a "how-to" book.

5 Pretend you are God. Rewrite 4 above.

CHAPTER NINETEEN:
SYMBOL CRASHES

Symbolism is the mathematics of literature, the pure equation: CONCRETE X = ABSTRACT Y.

Symbols can make you seem much, much smarter than you may in fact be. At the very least, they can make your story seem to be about much, much more than perhaps it is. Dear reader, in short, using symbols is the difference between the commercial hack and the true artiste.

Or, as my sweet childhood chums James Baldwin and Denis Johnson and John Barth (or was it Robert Coover?) might have once said to me, "Symbolism is pretty important." (No, it was Kazuo Ishiguro (note to self: check references.))

The beautiful thing about symbols is that they let you say what you want to say in an elegant shorthand. In fact, they can say things you may not quite know how to say. For example, I may know that a character is a real sleazebag, but I don't want to come right out and say that—where's the fun in that?—or I might not even know exactly what kind of a sleazebag he is. If I have him carry a big sewer rat in a tiny cage everywhere he goes, though—well, that sewer rat becomes the SYMBOL of all that is sleazy about this man. It may take a while, but your audience will figure out that this man is not perhaps the nicest man in the story. If he wears clothes made out of the pelts of other dead sewer rats, your reader will know that he is *very* sleazy, and has been for a long time (because he has "owned" so many sewer rats (which equals sleaze, remember) that he can make a suit out of their skins). See what qualities of awfulness you can convey through a SYMBOL?

You can of course EXTEND a symbol (in mathematical terms, this would be CONCRETE X + 1 = ABSTRACT Y +1). Let us say that our sleazy man is at an opera, and has begun to fantasize the most awful things about the lead soprano. If he leaves the rat in the cage, that is a SYMBOL that he will only fantasize, this night. If he lets his sewer rat out of the cage, though, that SYMBOLIZES that he will give his unwholesome side free reign and go backstage and actually do the awful things he was thinking. If, before he can leave his seat, the sewer rat leaps up and rips out his throat, the smart reader will know that you have just suggested SYMBOLICALLY that unwholesome desires can "kill" the one who has them. And you never had to *say* any of this directly! *Vive la symbolisme!*

Now, all of the above was exploring a CONTEXTUAL SYMBOL. In some stories, giant caged sewer rats could SYMBOLIZE love, or confusion, or the feeling of déjà vu you sometimes get while watching an episode of *Just Shoot Me* (note to self: insert mediocre sitcom of the future here). Sewer rats can be associated with many different ideas, depending on the CONTEXT in which they are used. Contextual symbols are powerful, but not as powerful as universal symbols.

A UNIVERSAL SYMBOL is a thing that is always linked with the same idea, no matter what the context. Water, for example, is a UNIVERSAL SYMBOL and it has always been linked with satisfaction (because water quenches thirst, which always symbolizes longing). For example, if a character in a story is thirsty, that character is really full of longing, either for his third-grade teacher, or inner peace, or that perfect day when he hit the homerun *and* got kissed by Christine Wentz. But if, in a different circumstance, a character is swimming, that character is *satisfied,* even if he or she does not appear to be so. Look, for example, at the end of *The Awakening,* when Edna Pontellier swims out to her death. She may seem unhappy, and does in fact die, but she is *satisfied,* even though she commits suicide rather than live in a male-dominated society that will allow no deviation from its rigid notions of what woman's role should be, which you would think would be evidence of her profound *dissatisfaction* especially her killing herself and all, but ah, ah! Chopin is smart, and puts her in water at the end, which we know symbolizes satisfaction. You see how SYMBOLISM can add complexity to your work?

Sometimes, when you look back on them, events in your life can seem fraught with symbolic significance.

An example, for instructional purposes only:

One day when Miranda was two and Chloe was four I left for cigarettes and did not come home for a day. I ate dinner in a diner and I slept in my office and spent the next morning at the University library reading literary magazines looking for ideas and then I faked my way through an afternoon workshop and I drove home, nauseous and anxious.

I remember I thought things were about to change. I had put up a swingset just the week before.

As I pulled into the long, long driveway, I saw a terrible thing. The house, our house, began to fold up. The chimney flattened and dropped over, the roof folded up like wings and then slid down into the house, the walls collapsed, and as I continued up the drive, the house continued to dismantle itself and by the time I got there the porch had just shuttered in and the basement popped up like a box flattened and then folded one two three four folds in on itself until the whole house, our country house, was a thin paper envelope in the middle of a field.

The swingset was not there, as if it never had been.

I got out of the car. My hands trembled.

I picked up the envelope. The grass grew tall while I stood there.

In the middle of a wheat field I opened the envelope and read this note: "Abracadabra. I still love you. You can visit the girls this weekend."

Later, I could not find the car in the high wheat and it took me ten days to find my way back to town.

Only many laters later, sitting here in the motel, drunk I admit as a skunk, my Muse ignoring me, lying on her stomach on the bed her legs in the air swaying, listening to Roky Erickson sing about ghosts on her Walkman while she read Gardner's *The Art of Fiction* (I was and am curious as to whose library she has been raiding (have I already said that? Time is so confusing sometimes)), my stomach churning, did I realize: wheat, envelopes, vanishments. The symbolism was so clear, it was as if some larger malevolent force had peeked its head out through my monitor and grinned at me spitefully. I literally cried out and punched the computer off without saving anything. It is rare that I feel the shock of recognition, winsome reader. I don't much like it.

Anyhow. The novice writer may not be familiar with all of these UNIVERSAL SYMBOLIC EQUATIONS. And sometimes, writers and teachers don't give you straight answers, or have misunderstood the true origins of a symbolic relationship. Let me, pious readers, give you a quick rundown on the most common UNIVERSAL SYMBOLS!!

Black

This is one of the most misunderstood symbols, often associated with death. In fact, black symbolizes possibility, even hope. After all, black is the combination of all colors, all things (as opposed to white, which is its absence, and obviously symbolizes hopelessness). When people wear black to funerals, they are expressing their hope in an afterlife. Were I to dress a cowboy in a black hat, you would know that here was a man with possibilities. Many options. At my wedding, which was in the morning, I wore a white tuxedo. But that's real life, not fiction.

Sun

Because the sun is warm and it feels good to be warm we often associate the sun with happiness. Instead, however, the sun symbolizes weariness. Even as I type this it's 98 degrees outside. I wouldn't have even left my beautiful Moon Winx air conditioner if I hadn't run out of vodka and cigarettes. Outside, I swooned with heat. Becky the maid was carrying an armful of soiled linens out of Room 5. She studiously did not look my way. I could barely drag myself to my air-conditioned car to drive to the air-conditioned Osco and back. Right now I am very weary. And the whole time, I was aware of the sun beating down, beating down, beating down.

Snake

We often associate the snake with Satan, or evil, probably because of the Eden thing. Occasionally I have run into cultures for whom the snake is a phallic symbol. Both over-simplify. In fact, the snake symbolizes, very specifically, male impotence. Satan, after all, failed time and time again against God and his folks. And even though he won in Eden, sort of, he had to slide around on his belly for ever and ever. Never to rise. Need I say more? I have never seen a rigid snake, nor one pointing at a 45 or 90 degree angle, so the phallic association is clearly imprecise. When, in

Flannery O'Connor's story "The Life You Save May Be Your Own" a snake slithers across the road, that clearly symbolizes the main guy's (note to self: check his name (double note to self: make sure there is a snake slithering across the road in that story)) inability to achieve erection, which in turn is what makes him so nasty and why he abandons the mentally challenged peacock girl at the diner—fear of impotence (note to self: is this the right story? is this any story? if not, write it).

Green

Another color. Well, colors are often symbolic, and we need not belabor the obvious. Blue = duplicity. Yellow = heartbreak. Orange = sexual prowess. White = a peculiar kind of Western nausea. Purple = professional jealousy. Red = a near-fatal complacency. And green, lovely green, symbolizes love, of course, which is why traffic lights that are green mean *go!* (as in "Go drive to your lover's door right now, young lover!").

Late at night, as I cruise around town loaded, with the windows down and the cool night air rushing past me, drowning out all thought, I watch for green lights, gun the engine at the sign of a yellow, drift through reds with a strangled sob.

Porches

And what are porches if they are not portals, entry ramps to a new life, a place to repose, to collect, to move on, either in or out? Thus porches always symbolize the Moment of Grace, the divine presence entering one's life, blinding you with the possibility of change. Whether you sit on the porch for the rest of your life, or go in to the cool sweet darkness of the house, or out into the indifferent blister of the sun, that's up to you. On the porch (as in Moments of Grace) all things are possible.

Dog

And oh, that dog that knew its fate, that knew all things, that knew your mind, that forgave you your blindness, that leapt to death for you, that dog there frozen forever in flight above the hedge just before the U.S. Post Office cancels it forever, that dog there symbolizes Christ, as do all dogs. They are the divine spark in animal form, the Word made Flesh. This may seem sacrilegious at first, but trust me, the world over, it is the dog, not the calf or the lamb or the dove or any other creature, that is most often linked with holiness, with Christ's sacrifice. When you see a dog leap or snore or bark through a story, you know that writer is trying to make a point about the fallen world, about redemption, about Christ's presence in your life.

Envelopes

I like to think of unopened envelopes as symbolic of a model of the universe, a la Schroedinger's cat. The unopened envelope contains all possibilities at once. Well, maybe not all possibilities—the unopened envelope does not contain an elephant, though it might contain another envelope. Envelope-sized possibilities, then. Anything may be true of the written contents within. Thus, all things are true of the contents within. Conversely, the opened envelope is the reduction of possibilities to one. That is a rejection letter. That there is a love letter. That there is a letter that says, "I love you, but I reject you." That letter will never be anything else. It is fixed, now, was fixed the moment you decided to open it. Therefore, the fictional optimist will never open envelopes. She or he will let all letters pile up on the kitchen table, and live a happy life of infinite possibilities.

Mint

Cool and refreshing, right? Wrong! Mint symbolizes the artificiality of modern culture. Look at how many things you smell or ingest that have been *artifically* flavored or scented to resemble mint. Mint mouthwash, mint chip ice cream, mint toothpaste, mint cough drops, mint medicine, mint flavored condoms—there is something repulsive about such corruption. Any time a character in a novel brushes his or her teeth, you can just bet that person is not what he or she seems to be on the surface! Other characters, beware! Satan comes with the stink of mint surrounding him, not sulfur. Beware! (As an aside, don't you sometimes wish that characters in stories or books or even movies were aware of the symbolism that surrounds them? If I was a character in a story and somebody wearing a canary-yellow suit wanted to smear toothpaste over my dog, sitting on the sun-flooded porch, I'd do my level best to claw my way out of the narrative, and take the dog with me.)

Computers

It's a common mistake to associate computers with the inhuman, the mechanical, the cold calculating other. In fact, computers are wonderful symbols of the human self. The monitor is the id, the hard drive is the ego, and the keyboard is the superego. Thus, in the best fiction, the person sitting at a computer typing is really symbolic of the ways we constantly create and revise the self. The blown monitor is the end result of the id unleashed. The computer crashed is, of course, a symbol of untimely death.

Croquet Balls

As the croquet course is rigidly laid out, elegant in its geometry, it symbolizes the world, our ordered Universe. The croquet ball, nicked and buffeted by mighty mallets, not at all in control of its own destiny yet still capable of great harm, using other balls to advance, trapped in a desperate reel of promotion, the drive to succeed, to win, to triumph—you know who that is. Dear reader, that poor ball spinning through wickets and grazing stakes, that ball there is you.

EXERCISES

1 Think about the most traumatic moment of your life. What objects have you come to associate with that moment? Now think about your happiest moment. Now your scariest. Now your angriest. Etcetera and so on. Make a list of the things you associate with each moment. Now you have a PRIVATE SYMBOLIC VOCABULARY. Learn it well. Use it consistently. Everyone else will figure it out sooner or later.

2 Make sure that every person, place and thing in your story also has a symbolic value. This symbolic value can be minor. Look puzzled when somebody suggests you've written an allegory. Say, "It's all realism to me."

3 Take note of ten things on the drive to or from work (or the grocery store, or whatever). Now if those things were in a story, what would they symbolize? Is the trash by the side of the road a symbol of your character's cluttered mind, or the indifference of the modern world? Is the solid double line man's scarring of the natural world or symbolic of a particular marital union, unbroken? What about that elm tree? Strength or disease? That crow? Scavenger or survivor or both? Look at the world as if everything there had a secret message written just for you. Can you unlock the meaning of it? Is it a happy or sad message? Most importantly, who is sending it, and why now?

CHAPTER TWENTY:
THEME AND MEANING

Thankfully, this is an instruction manual, and thus has no theme. Stories, though, do need not just to be, but to be *about*. Here's why:

In real life, of course, there are no themes.

You may be tempted to look for unity, life lessons, epiphanies and resolutions, but none of it exists. Life is not *about* anything. It just is, in all of its awful wonder. That's why we have fiction, of course, to give us what our lives lack. We crave meaning in our fiction because our lives lack it utterly.

There is no lesson to be learned from my life, for example. You might think that the collapse of my marriage would be a defining moment, that what followed would be suffused with meaning, that those months upon months would have led to the dark, sad culmination of a logical sequence of events. It would even be pretty to think that I'd learned something about myself, that I was wiser, if sadder.

In truth, the days just keep happening. I was happy, and now I am not, and perhaps maybe someday I'll be happy again. Where is the lesson in that?

For a while there, the regular visits to and of my daughters ordered my weeks, and kept me, if not always grounded and sober, at least close enough to the ground to come down and walk on it with them for a while. The day before I was to pick them up, I would drink nothing but Gatorade and pop ginkgo biloba and vitamins c and e and rent wholesome movies and memorize the dialogue.

The day I was to meet them I would shave my Daddy Mask and put it on and practice smiling for a while. My mouth was like loose taffy on my stiff shiny face. Beneath the mask I could cry freely, and would not scare them with my tears. My Muse would sit on the edge of the tub, bored, making little mews of disgust whenever I would start to cry.

At their mother's request, I would not pick them up at their new house, and I was a tiny bit relieved at this—it would have been terribly hard to see their new bedrooms, their new toys, their new books and games, no hint of my taste or presence in any of it. That sounds more selfish than I mean it. I mean simply that that they could have lives without me was an agony. I mean simply that I missed them.

Instead, following instructions Penelope would mail to me the week before (and which would self-destruct in thirty seconds, natch), I drove around town for a while, stopping at third stoplights, taking the fourth lefts, going 1.2 miles past the gas station. At the end of the directions I pulled the car over to the side of the road. Sometimes I would find a large white box tied with pink ribbon. I would pull the ribbon and the walls would fall away. They would be waiting for me inside, grinning. Sometimes I would hear Chloe or Miranda then say, "Hi, Daddy," from the back seat, as if they had been there all along. Sometimes I would hear them kicking at the trunk and I would open it up and a hundred helium balloons would dart out sperm-like into the sky and there they would be, my impossibly happy daughters, laughing at the look of startlement I made with my Daddy Mask.

Some days we would just drive out into the country, looking for bluebirds and red earth. Some days we would play putt-putt golf, or go to a fair, ride the rides. My Muse often accompanied us. The girls mostly ignored or did not see her. I was glad she was there, though. It was almost like a family, me in my Daddy Mask (slipping), the girls in their Daughter Masks, my Muse drifting along distracted.

It ended one sad day at the top of a Ferris wheel. The gears of normality were grinding. My gyroscopes needed re-calibration. There was a pulse in me, a vacillation that matched the neon rhythm of the Moon Winx moon. I wanted to be there for them, wanted them desperately in my life, but I knew I had been in Room 6 too long. It had become the only place I knew, my conversation with the walls and the self the only thing I spoke fluently. Foreboding shuddered through me as we lurched slowly up, and up.

At the top of the Ferris wheel we looked out at the county, the green hills, the red earth, the rivers and quarries. I lifted my arm to point and say something educational and brushed my mask. It swung off half my face, then fell clattering through the spokes and girders of the Ferris wheel, cracking apart. My Muse swung out of the car and clambered down like a spider monkey, but it was too late. My daughters stared at me in horror. They saw what I was. Then they took off their Daughter Masks and threw them out the car and we listened to them shatter and fall, like porcelain ground beneath heels. And I saw what they were. We stared at each other, weeping. The Ferris wheel began to move again. My Muse met us with an arm full of shards. When she saw our naked faces she dropped them and turned away.

I have not seen my daughters since.

And where is the meaning in that?

All that having been committed to paper, let me now tell you the secret no other writer will tell you, dear reader, because I love you, because I want you to succeed: as the product of a single patri/matriarchal author figure, theme is overrated.

Nine times out of ten in this postmodern world, your reader is going to assume the responsibility of cramming his or her own interpretation down the throat of your story anyway, so why bother? (Don't think about that tenth time. I don't write with a thought in my head beyond plot and character and pretty language, and I don't believe any writer who says they do otherwise.)

The first trick, of course, is to have lots of things happening in your fiction for readerly minds to fasten upon. I like to kill off a sizable chunk of my cast in certain books, and to do so in creative, almost ridiculous ways. So that patriotic curmudgeon gets speared by his own flagpole in a tornado, impaled overnight in the front yard, the flagpole sticking straight up into the air, his MIA-POW flag fluttering proudly. Now, I know this is ironic, but I don't know what it means beyond that. But did I get feedback from the various (many!) editors and agents that read (and rejected!) the manuscript! A brilliant condemnation of war! (but!) A pathetic leftist attack on our Our Armed Forces! (thus no!) An almost existential view of the universe! (and yet!) To tell the truth, when Penelope and I lived on 13th Street and I was writing that story, the Vietnam vet who lived across the street from us flew that flag every day, which I could see from my front room study as I typed and stared out the window. Also, I liked the black of the flag. I thought about making the flag a Jolly Roger. Things were not going well for us then. This was the house before the last house (see Chapter Seven, Setting); it was the dark horizon before the roll of thunder before the flicker of lightning before the storm; it was the elegant hand flourish of distraction before the rabbit is unvanished from the not-empty hat. In response to my inarticulate irks and quirks (my unarticulated insecurities) I could feel Penelope growing ever more distant, more distracted, and I pulled further back in response, which made her withdraw even more. It was as though each of us wanted the other to be the one to say the word that would finally, irrevocably, fuck everything up. Instead, we moved. So as I wrote that book, my mood was bleak, and the Jolly Roger seemed morbidly appropriate. But while that would have been funnier, it would also have been harder to interpret. In other words, dear readers, while *you* don't have to think too hard about what stuff in a story means, you *do* have to write with an eye toward the fact that *other* people will be doing just that!

I insist on un-meaning.

And your readers will take care of theme for you. They will invest your stories with meaning where there was no meaning. That's how much they crave it! Leftist attacks? Existentialism? I was just trying to be ironic, and I liked the color black. Don't try to figure out what your stories are about—let your readers do the hard work for you. Just get in the ballpark, and let their fertile imaginations go to work. Some writers hate critics—I say God bless them.

(Note to self: oh, bleak. When will it end?)

Of course, getting in the ballpark can be difficult. It's often closed for repairs, or the ball club is on the road, or you're there at noon and it's a night game (see Chapter XX: Extending a Metaphor). To that end, let me suggest a few broad subjects or ideas you should *not* explore—they've been done to death.

(Oh, where is the meaning in this?)

Ten Over-Rated Themes:

I EARTH IS REALLY A GIANT TROUT FARM

I think the best "giant trout farm" novel I ever read was Tim Parrish's *This Earth, This Trout Farm.* Some themes are untouchable because they've been done brilliantly by a master. This is one of them. Untouchable, I tell you.

2 DEATH IS REALLY A BRILLIANT STAND-UP COMIC
AND WE ARE JUST TOO STUPID TO GET HIS BEST BITS

Some themes are difficult to address not because of the one definitive treatment, but because of the exhaustiveness of many treatments. I've seen this theme explored from every angle—from the point of view of death, of the stupid audience, of God as comedy club owner—and to every logical conclusion—we need to go to more comedy clubs, we need to stop going to comedy clubs, what we really need are LAUGH and APPLAUSE signs on our deathbeds, et cetera. And after you've seen the same characters and ideas explored by everyone from Pirandello and Poe and Shakespeare to Jong and Hijuelos and Gordimer and Stegner and Nabokov, well, why bother? Been there, read that.

3 PHYSICS IS FAITH

Note to self:

4 CONSPIRACY THEORIES ARE INVENTED BY SECRET
GOVERNMENT AGENCIES THAT WANT US TO FOCUS
ON RIDICULOUS THEORIES WHILE THEY RULE THE
WORLD, ET CETERA

Of course John F. Kennedy was shot by a single gunman named Lee Harvey Oswald. There are no aliens. The simplest explanations are always the true ones. The government just wants to distract you.

5 ALL YOU NEED IS A DOG

Nothing should end like this. A good person would have saved him. A good person would have done something about everything.

6 NO THINGS BUT IN IDEAS

7

As my good friend Sherman Alexie Tim Gautreaux Victor LaValle Joey Manley Yesho Atil Walter Mosely Ha Jin Stephen Dixon Stephen Dobyns Leonard Michaels Charles D'Ambrosio Jhumpa Lahiri Francine Prose Peggy Vices Leigh-Ann Alan Colleen Claudia Sam Ron Shel Walter Eric Alicia Lisa Tim Mindy Kim Jeannie Randy Mark Kathy Mary Harry Jen Steve Jen Don Diane Hank Phil Jon Joan says, "

8

9

Note to self:

10

EXERCISES

CHAPTER TWENTY-ONE:
MAKING IT

Let it be said that I write this chapter against the best advice of my Muse, who refuses to be present as I type this. We argued long into the night. It is her opinion that a chapter like this not only has nothing to do with Art but is in fact irresponsible. I report this opinion out of respect to her.

She was shaking with anger or despair or both when she left me.

Each day, she reminds me more and more of Penelope. Something in the eyes.

I don't know where my Muse goes when she goes. She took a few twenties out of my wallet and shrugged into her leather jacket and exited out into the dark of the night. A light rain falls. Steam rises from the puddles. I am alone, and lonesome unto death.

I must tell you this.

As much as they try to tell you otherwise, most writers are not trying to make Art. They are trying to pay the rent, or to get famous, or to make all those assholes in high school sorry they ever humiliated him or her at assembly, or to get back at their parents for some real or imagined damage, or to convey important coded messages to foreign powers, or to convince the aliens to spare him or her when they come to enslave the planet. But rarely do the writers talk about creating Art, and I don't trust any writer who uses the A-word, and neither should you. Art is what other people decide is beautiful and lasting, and that always changes, so you shouldn't even worry about it.

What you should worry about as a writer is making it.

Making it, making it, making it: publish, get grants, land cushy teaching gigs, write movie scripts, get interviewed, get money, get famous. That's what you want. Baby, baby, baby, what you need to do is make it, be making it, get made. Rung by rung and reader by reader and buck by buck you want to climb that ladder, cultivate that audience, rake in those royalty checks. Making it, making it, baby baby baby baby! Anyone who tells you otherwise is just trying to keep you down, and this, *this* is why you don't ever find any writing books that are worth a damn. Those writers don't want the competition!

Me, I have nothing to lose.

Me, I respect and love you, gentle readers.

Now this may come as a shock to you. You may resist the notion. You may say that you're above all that. But picture this: you may temporarily be disappointed with yourself or the world, but you will have a shelf full of books and royalty checks coming in. And if you are one of those people with principles or somesuch, try to fool yourself into thinking that you still have noble aspirations. Art is long. Eventually, your self-loathing will diminish.

The more bitter you become, the more you hate yourself, the more you can be sure you're doing the right things. Success is yours, if you work hard enough at it.

There will be hard work involved, of course. You will have to write a lot, and then you will have to work hard to find an agent and/or an editor (and you will have many agents and many editors and they will help you get published and take money from you and move on if you test their patience), and then you will have to go on reading tours and book tours and signings and reading parties and after when maybe you would prefer to be at home with your pregnant wife but really you can't *make it* without putting the work in. The most work, though, is not in the writing, not in the business side, but in the schmoozing.

You should kiss ass shamelessly, the way some men date: pucker up for every single person of note or potential note that you meet. Some will be repelled and will reject you, but someone—my life on this—someone will respond favorably, and your career will have officially begun. But your work isn't over yet! It's just begun! Now you have to network—hit the writing circuit and repeat as necessary.

It may be necessary to go to bed with someone to get the kind of fame you want. For this reason, I always carried whipped cream, handcuffs, a bottle of tequila, twelve condoms, a banana, and four silk scarves on my person at all times at every writing conference I attended. Some people I know also brought Polaroid cameras, but blackmail, while effective, is just too distasteful for my stomach to wrap its head around.

Mostly, though, lying is the only really necessary ingredient to success. For God's sake, don't write an honest review. Blurb your brains out. Praise, flatter, shake hands, extend compliments, smile, smile, smile. All the while, know that you are doing a Corleone: "I will do this thing for you. Some day, I may ask you to do a little favor for me in return. On that day, you will do whatever I ask of you." (Note to self: rent *The Godfather* to check dialogue. (Note: rent VCR.)) Some days, niceness is the most effective way to get what you want. On those days, be nice. Dear reader, I have made it, and my success is all I have now in this room, and it *is* enough, and I tell you this truly, it makes me warm or at least provides the semblance of warmth, which if you don't think about it is really the same thing.

Still, sometimes, it may be necessary to sabotage even as you flatter. Be ready to ruin lives, oh-my-gentlest-of-readers. If they can't rebound, if they can't successfully check your efforts, then they didn't want to make it enough. I try not to destroy the careers of my students, of course, because who knows, they may be a big help to me further on down the road, and besides, they don't really have careers yet.

The perfect example of this is Andrew Shay, who went on to big things, and was a sweet man the whole time. How kind he was to us when our children were born, and various times over the years, dropping in unannounced, calling on Penelope while I was on the road. Later, famous, mentioning my name in interviews, or telling me about some contest or other I might want to enter. I have not heard much from him lately, now that Penelope and I have separated. But he has been a good friend to us down the years.

He will, I confess, always be that goofy twenty-year-old in my head, always hanging around the house and pestering me until Penelope would shrug and divert him, take him into the kitchen to help her cook a meal or down to her workshops to show him some trick or other. Andrew, always saying something inappropriate or naïve. He has cultivated the look of the aging hipster now (his teeth growing whiter every day), but how well I remember his white socks and black Reeboks, his acned complexion, his generic black glasses, his desperate need to please. In my mind, no matter how many interviews he does with Barbara Walters, I see that goofy kid in his first workshop actually peeing himself (I think) at some theatrical attention-getter of mine, and I have to smile.

I admit I sometimes wishthingswer

[Here the text as printed was an unreadable garble of smiley face icons and other electronic gibberish—one suspects some sort of electrical failure Gus didn't have the time to correct—A.S.]

The point is, had I been another kind of ladder-climber, I could have sensed his talent (he was talented, though no more or less than scores of my most talented students down the years) and I could have done my best to squash him. How contemptible, though! And how many favors I would have missed down the years. Mostly, though, it's a matter of principle to me, a line I will not cross. I despise those professors who destroy writers further down the ladder than them—destroy those above you.

How, you ask?

And here my honesty must fail you, and here I must rescind my promise to tell you everything, oh my reader. Who knows but that you won't take these tools that I give you and use them against me someday? Would I really put a loaded gun in all of your hands, not knowing if each and every one of you was completely composed, sanity-wise? In fact, the saner you are, the more pragmatic you might be, the more likely I'd become the victim of my very own words.

I'm sorry to fail you, readers.

As I typed the word fail, you may be interested to know, my Muse returned. She's obviously drunk, and her clothes and hair stink of cigarettes. She will not look at me. Instead, she locks herself in the bathroom. She throws up for hours. She will not unlock the door.

EXERCISES

1 For a week, practice flattering every single person that you meet, from the woman who works in City Hall and takes your water bill every month to the bag boy at the grocery store to crazy old Chicken George who stands in the middle of intersections and balances beer cans on his head. You'll be ready for your next writer's conference.

2 Read everything by everyone who will be leading a workshop or presenting a paper at your next conference. Think of something nice to say about each of those works. Think of one smart question to ask about each of those works. Practice saying, "I'm a big fan," and sounding like you mean it. Repeat as necessary. HOT TIP: Don't waste too much time schmoozing with the really big names. Instead, focus on lots of mid-range writers who may hit it big later. When they do, you'll be glad you took the time to kiss up back when they were relative nobodies!

3 Memorize ten politically correct jokes, ten offensive jokes, and ten neutral comedy bits by obscure comics. Go to your nearest comedy club to steal material your audience won't have heard. Tell jokes. Making people laugh ingratiates them to you. Make sure you don't confuse a politically correct audience with an "old boys" audience.

4 Be prepared to go to bed with a wide variety of partners. If previously heterosexual or homosexual, try to imagine yourself as bisexual. Masturbate while looking at pictures of all different body types and ethnicities. Gain as much

practical experience as possible. Apply your experience as indicated. Refuse to answer your editor when she asks you if she's supposed to be frustrated that she doesn't know how much of this applies to your own life. Watch your career skyrocket!!!

PART THREE

Revise

"I am not what I am."
—*Othello,* 1.1.67

CHAPTER TWENTY-TWO:
CRISIS

As I type this I have lost all sense of time. The curtains are drawn, the room is frigid, I hear the thump of a stereo's bass (the woofer? all knowledge escapes me) somewhere and so guess it is night, possibly late at night. Probably. The later it is, the louder it gets around here, until there is a sudden mysterious hush just before dawn. The night-people crack up or collapse and the morning-people are still deep in the most intense of their dreams, the ones they will remember. The sound of traffic ceases, and if there are birds or raccoons the thrum of my air conditioner masks any sounds they might make. Even my Muse is still, sitting in a lotus position in the corner or curled up in the desk drawer with the phone book and the Gideon's.

Quiet unfolds as if it came from inside you and you feel like you could close your eyes and stop being in your body, that you could be quietness flapping out like an endless blanket out and out and out to cover up the whole world in a sweet whispered woolen hush.

Then the cigarette you'd been holding burns down to your knuckles and you curse and your eyes snap open and you are you again, totally fucked and fucked up, and a car door slams, and it all starts happening again.

As I type this my Muse opens one eye and scowls at me, then stands up out of her lotus as graceful as water pouring back up out of a glass into a pitcher. Usually she will ignore me, put her headphones on or turn on the television or knit something, which is an odd thing to see, my postpunk black-clad fiercer-than-thou Muse knitting Muse-sized sweaters she never wears but that make you wonder what sort of life she wants to be living ten years from now.

This night she goes to the dresser and pulls out a suitcase and then opens the bottom drawer and starts putting everything back into the suitcase, strategically ripped tee shirts and lovingly washed fishnet stockings (and you never think about her washing them in the sink, do you, do you, when you see them on, you never think about her hand-wringing them, hanging them on the radiators to dry, you just ogle her legs, don't you, even though she's your Muse, for God's sake, oh, don't you!) and surprisingly white panties (Hanes Her Way) and a beautifully worn leather jacket and a perfect pale prom dress and a dazzling white wedding dress and sneakers and combat boots and pumps and more and more and more and finally I say, "Hey." I'm still sitting at the computer. My fingers are still on the keyboard.

She looks over her shoulder at me. "Man, you just don't fucking get it, do you?"

I scratch the back of my neck. "Um," I say.

She goes into the bathroom, comes back out with an armful of shampoo and conditioner and deodorant and tampons and panty shields and perfume and mouthwash and soaps for her face and her body and special sponges and brushes and massagers and other instruments she doesn't let me see before she dumps it all in the suitcase and snaps the lid down.

"Hey!" I say.

"What?" she says. She stands next to her suitcase with her hands on her hips. She's wearing ripped-to-hell jeans and a plain black cut-off tee shirt and motorcycle boots. Her face is scrubbed free of makeup and her hair is pulled back in a ponytail. She puts on a pair of sunglasses.

"What?" she says.

"You can't just leave me," I say.

She snorts. "I don't know why I stayed as long as I fucking did," she says. "You'll never figure it out."

"Figure what out?" I say. I am desperate to begin a conversation. As long as we're talking, she can't go.

"Look around you, Gus," she says. "Where are we?"

I look around. "Didn't I pretty much say all that in Chapter Seven? Setting?"

She slaps her forehead with her palm. "The climax," she says, and she makes it sound obscene, definitely non-sexual. "We're at the crisis, the climax. The only thing left is the fucking resolution."

"I get it," I say.

She looks at me wearily. "You haven't 'gotten it' ever," she says.

"Okay, you're right," I say. "That's why I need you. You can't leave me like this. You can see what a mess I am. I admit I don't get it. Maybe I never have. So enlighten me. Show me. What don't I get?"

"It's the climax, for God's sake, Gus!"

I slap the table angrily. "I know that, all right?"

"There are only fifteen pages left!"

I look at my computer monitor anxiously. "Well, I didn't know that," I say. "All the more reason to stay and see me through!"

She takes her sunglasses off. "There are only fifteen pages left," she says gently. "This is it. It's all denouement from here on out. *Think* about it," she says, and her eyes are so sad and so full of pity it breaks my heart and makes me very very afraid.

"You love me," I say suddenly. "That's what I didn't get."

She puts her sunglasses on. "Jesus, Gus, you are one stupid motherfucker, you know that?"

"Okay, wait, don't go, I'm sorry, that was stupid."

She picks up her suitcase.

"Don't go," I say.

She walks to the door.

"Please don't leave me. I'm begging you. Please."

She turns.

"Gus," she says. "A vision. Behold."

She opens the door.

Outside it is white-hot afternoon and heat and light swarm in the room and then I hear the creak of footsteps moving unsteadily across a sagging porch and I see faces like flowers float into the room and dazzle me, swimming and hovering before my face, and there first are my girls all grown up, beautiful and sad, white veils over their faces, and they turn and they say "I do," to the handsome boy-flower-faces that bob next to them and all the faces are happy and loving but sad, too, and they drift up to the ceiling and through it and then a parade of flower-faces about the size of tulips marches burbly by, my ex-students, sizing me up, pursing their leafy lips, some loving, some bitter, and then there is one flower that is Andrew Shay and a knot as big as a croquet ball swells above his left eye and he looks at me with a swarm of feelings like bees wriggling across his face and last at the last a sunflower radiant there is Penelope, bumping in gently behind Andrew and they both whirl around my face as if in waltz time and Penelope is so sweetly herself and so hurt and sad that I almost get it I almost think I understand.

It's on the tip of my tongue.

But then there at the last I feel some gaseous unease in my stomach like I'm about to puke or God forbid lose control of my bowels which would be disgusting especially with all of the flower-balloon-faces especially with my Penelope so near and Shay there looking like he'd like to see that, and suddenly I hear my Muse say, "Lord, why can't you just *see*," and I hear the sound of a door closing forever and then each face pops like the sun going out and Penelope's face goes last with a sound like a cork expelled and I say, "Jesus, don't go," and then I am alone again in the dark, the door closed, the lights out, my hands trembling, and I almost get it. It's on the tip of my tongue.

I almost get it.

CHAPTER TWENTY-THREE:
REVISION

Given the chance, I would do everything differently. I would explode the world, rip apart the universe at the seams to undo all that I have done, to change all that is. I swear to you I would dismantle yours and every other life, oh my gentle readers, if it would mean my family was not lost to me, my love, my only real happiness defiled. I would foul all of creation to unfoul my one tiny corner of it.

That Alabama morning in the cool of the breeze, the screwdriver sickly sweet in the back of my throat, kissing Penelope on the throat, the collarbone, the crook of the elbow, the back of the knee, up her thighs, that was the moment I should have burned into my memory. Her arms raised above her head as I pulled the nightgown off, her brown eyes flecked with yellow and splinters of darker brown gazing at me wickedly, measuring my worth, not then finding me wanting—those eyes I should have imagined on me everywhere, all the time.

It was already too late, of course. Even then, my flaws were apparent. Drinking vodka on a Sunday morning, encouraging the worst in my students and myself, daring Penelope to suggest the obvious, that I check into a program, do the Twelve Steps, rehab, anything. Daring her to tell me to get the help I so obviously needed. I heard Andrew's steps on the porch long after I had thought he was gone, and I should have realized then how dissolute my life had become, how much I was corrupting a young talent, too—he was so pliable, then, and my ego must have needed a sidekick.

On that pure clear morning with the deep blue curtains drawn and lifting lightly in the breeze I strained above her and she rocked below me, and we conceived our first child, and this I would not undo, never, this joy I would not ever write out of the universe. But the moment was tainted in so many ways that I long to undo. I would not be drunk when we conceived, and I would not be away on a book tour some nine months later. It would be me, not one of my ex-students, in her hospital room holding her hand and putting a wet cloth on her forehead that night after she had delivered our first child into the world alone. I would be the first one to hold my child, to change her diaper, to fall asleep exhausted in a chair by my wife's bed, the baby finally sleeping on my chest. The night—I've imagined it so often— would pass like a fever, nurses creaking in and out of the dark of the room, the baby wailing every hour or so, my jacket balled up as a pillow.

Further back: the night I proposed, drunk, Otis Redding on the stereo. A spontaneous proposal we called it later, but what does that mean? That I needed to be drunk to say "Marry me," that I had no ring, that I was desperate, and foolish, that even the start of our lives together was flawed, cracked. Time, unbend yourself. I would ride back on your dripping curves. I would buy a ring, plan a speech, pick a moment, light a thousand candles, spread rose petals, saturate that generic apartment with light and perfume, leave the Otis Redding (I got lucky there), leave unopened the first bottle of wine. Sober, perfect, tender, I would start everything over, perfectly.

But why start there?

Further back, further back: oh, who knows where to start? What shames and desires, what toilet training mysteries, made me what I am today? Further back, further back, further back: who knows which dominos to shift about? Who knows what the first domino was? Was it that day my dog died so horribly, the image of his carcass burned behind my eyes that made each successive day taste like ash? Can you explain a life gone wrong with a dead dog?

To this day I mystify myself beyond all reckoning.

How tempting it would be to blame someone else, anyone else, to create for myself an antagonist, a dark opposite. Doesn't it seem sometimes as if there must surely have been some malevolent force conspiring against you? Your flaws so large, true, but that large? Large enough to leech the goodness out of your life? So terrible that they left you here?

The problem with hindsight is that it's *only* twenty-twenty. How can you see the exact moment where things went wrong? How can you divine the single moment that shaped your personality? How can you change the awful things you did and said and were and still keep the good? What if it was only the terrible mistakes you made and harms you inflicted on others that allowed something as special as your daughter to be born into the world? Would anyone, even your wife, even the mother of your child, say it was worth it? Would you?

In a different world, the notes I wrote her after Chloe was born, so lyrical and honest, would have worked on some sympathetic part of her soul. They did not, as if she never read them. Andrew was always around the house back then—I should have given the letters to him to give to Penelope instead of leaving them for her on the kitchen table or her pillow. Oh, what am I thinking? In a better world, I would not have relied on the written word—damn my words, curse all of my words, what good have they ever done me?—but would instead have just talked to her, gotten us into therapy, been more honest. In a pure sweet world her love and the mere presence of my children would have been enough to center me always and forever. I curse myself as I curse my words. I curse all that the world has become. There was no conspiracy—there is no antagonist here but me.

How awful to realize that you are the secret villain of your life, not its hero at all!

Where I am now it's noisy all the time, more so at night, my neighbors always partying or arguing, their televisions too loud, their dogs too miserable, their lives too frightening to allow three AM to sneak up on them asleep. Now that I'm alone, now that even my Muse has left me, I've taken to sleeping during the day, and staying up with the rest of them, grimly. I crack a bottle of vodka and some nights lay out a few lines of coke or speed and turn on the television or the computer and put on some headphones and loud music and lurch into midnight, eyes wide open. Some nights I crawl behind the wheel and cruise. This is all easy to do when you no longer give a damn really where or how you spend the rest of your life. I'm so far gone the cops can't see me—I have yet to be pulled over. Other cars and pedestrians sense me but do not see me. Despair renders invisibility.

When light bleeds into the air around me, saturating the thin membrane between here and there, I spin the wheel and steer my boat of a car back to the Moon Winx Motel. I do not park but stop, somewhere, in the lot. Spill out, puke, bleed, swallow it all, bark back at the dogs that bark at me, puke on and bite at the hands that reach, and shudder back into my room to collapse on the bed. I am then mercifully not in the world (though I would not say what I do is sleep) for a number of hours, and then I suffer the sear of a few sober hours. On Wednesday and Thursday I shake and medicate until it's time for my workshops. We all endure that somehow. Then off to the bars for the post-workshop bloodletting and/or wound dressing. Then again. And again. And again.

There are still moments for me, sometimes, that shudder with clarity, as lucid as ice cracking out of a tray. In those moments I imagine picking up a pen and unwriting my past, my self, unwriting back and back and back to my childhood, to the womb, to the genetic strands that first entangled me here. Unwrite it all.

Some nights I can almost see us, in some other universe, all of us together again, renting a house in a sleepy town in Illinois. I will be teaching composition and survey courses—anything but creative writing—at a sleepy community college. Penelope will be working part-time in a library, then staying at home full-time to raise the girls and to store up magic. We will have a dog named Otis who will be sweet and stupid and loving and the house will always be dirty and falling down, and I will have planted bulbs each fall and will watch them come up each spring, and we will fill bird feeders and keep track of what we see in a birder's book and our neighbors will be friendly and warm, good wholesome people in a safe, quiet town in a sedate fold of the earth along the Illinois River, and there we will live out our days and our nights and there our girls will grow up and grow strong and be happy and there I am even now writing an interesting book and look, see, there is Penelope, rolling up her sleeves, tipping her hat, pulling miracles that are books that are words that are wonderful out of the thin clear air.

And if you don't know what any of that has to do with revision, then you haven't been paying attention. Go back. Go back, and do it again. Go back and do it right this time, Goddamn it dear reader, go back and do it right.

CHAPTER THE LAST: DENOUEMENT

Dear, dear readers. If you're here, then I'm not quite as alone as I feel. I must confess I feel very lonely. There is no reason really to stay sober, as I think it's summer, and I don't teach, or at least I am not teaching now, and have not for several weeks, how many I do not know. And yet anyway I find I can't work up the energy to get drunk, or when I do I too easily drink myself sober. I haven't bought a newspaper in weeks. I don't think the TV works. I think I have broken it somehow in the last few days. I'm not sure why I think that. But I feel sure of it. I didn't know Frank Sinatra had died until my dealer told me a few weeks ago. He also told me that someone named Phil Hartman died. I don't know who that was. My dealer seems only to read the obituaries, or at least that's the only news he passes along to me. I wonder if he's a cop? He's obsessed with death the way I think some undercover cops must be. If he is, he hasn't busted me yet and always seems to have very good cocaine and so-so pot.

I miss the Muse. I can't even call her "my" anymore. She's probably already moved on. Working with someone who's working on a bestseller.

I can not shake the feeling that everything could have been different. Maybe not with Penelope. But here, now, in this motel room. The vision. I can't help but feel that if I had just done something, something there at the near-end...but what that might have been escapes me.

Let me tell you about my dreams. ("I had a dream, the other night / Everything was still. / I dreamed I saw Susannah / coming down the hill.") Or at least a dream.

Last night I dreamt that I was sitting on a metal folding chair in front of a plain glass window. It was sunny outside. This was no house I'd ever been in, no lawn I'd ever looked out at. It was very peaceful. The sky was very blue. The grass was very green. The clouds, when they passed, were pretty and puffy and very white.

Suddenly a black croquet ball exploded through the window and hit me in the head and bounced straight up in the air. I fell over backwards with a clatter and lay on the floor with my legs tangled in the chair and looked up and there stood Penelope above me. She caught the ball as it fell towards me again. She plucked it out of midair. She palmed it. She passed her other hand over that hand and smiled at me and then opened her empty hands. Gone.

"You saved me," I said. Even then I felt my forehead throb.

"Almost," she said. "I tried."

Then everything spun away.

Then I was lying on my back in a dark field and it was raining croquet balls. They bounced like hailstones on and around me. One bounces on my chest, twice, thud thud, and then looks at me with croquet eyes and says, "Lord, what a dork. I think you'd better wake up now."

And I did.

It's too late to look for meaning, I know. I don't know why I feel compelled to tell you about my dreams, dear reader. I used to hate it when Penelope tried to tell me about yet another interminable illogical dream—they're always far more fascinating to the dreamer than to the non-dreamer. More fascinating to the dreamer than to the dreamed.

I'm really losing it.

I had a theory I would sometimes tell Penelope about, mostly just to talk my way through it, to hear the sound of it as told by my own voice. I thought maybe it was something I'd use in a book, but I never did.

I believed then and still do now that there are parallel universes (see Chapter Eighteen: Points of View). Every choice ever made spawns another universe, so that there are infinite universes out there. The first amoeba could split lengthwise or widthwise, and two more universes. Down to me, yesterday, you can have wheat or white with your runny eggs. Two more universes. In both I probably regret my choice. I believe that physics supports this theory. So that really, all things are possible. If you happen to make a mistake, there's another universe where you did not, where you are happy. To me, it was a very optimistic view of life.

"Jesus, that's sad," Penelope would say to me.

Somewhere, though, we are still together, and happy. In fact, in lots of universes we are together and happy, in an almost infinite variety of ways. If I happen to be unhappy in this one, it comforts me to think of all the other me's who are so happy in so many other worlds.

I think of my little subset of universes, the unhappy Gus's, as divergent, not the norm. If we could all get together, all of us Gus's, and have a picnic or cookout or something, me and those like me would definitely be shunned by the normal happy Gus's in their sunny shirts and nice haircuts. We, the screwed up and the scary, the malformed Gus's, would guzzle beer in a corner of the yard and curse and spit and pretend that we didn't care what the other Gus's thought. We'd slouch up to the grill and ignore the small talk about how they quit smoking or what Chloe and Miranda did yesterday and some well-adjusted Gus would slap a steak done just the way we like it onto our plate and look at us with concern and we'd go inside to the living rooms and kitchens and storerooms while the Happy Gus's stayed outside.

Hovering in the doorways, the Conflicted Gus's would peer in at us, torn, sympathetic, maybe even attracted to our misery, our foul malaise, but just hovering there on the edge. Whom would we hate more, the clean crisp Happy Gus's or those shame-faced cruisers, those scene-sidlers?

In the basement the Other Gus's would be indulging in some Other Perversity: watching movies of Unspeakable

Otherness projected on a dirty sheet and eventually masturbating and fellating each other—oh, even we would avoid the basement. In the attic, the Zealot Gus's would be kneeling in their brown robes, flagellating each other and chanting unceasingly. Even we steered clear of the attic.

We'd turn on the TV and watch Jerry Springer or Access Hollywood or something while the Happy Gus's stood in the sun and played whiffle-ball and shook their heads about us, the dark cousins, the brooders, the fuck-ups. "What can you do?" they'd say, and "There but for the grace of God," and "It could just as easily have been us, you know," and inside in the dark in front of the television our hearts would break and we'd put the steaks aside barely eaten and crack open another beer and light another cigarette and clear off the coffee table and do lines of coke and heroin and settle into the blue buzz of the dark inside.

I don't know how all of this will end.

Yesterday I saw the abductee, the UFO Girl. This was by accident (I think) in a diner just down the street from the Moon Winx. I cannot remember the name of this diner. Every four months it closes for a few weeks and then re-opens with a new name and a new owner but with exactly the same red vinyl booths and green stools at the white counter and the same runny eggs and the same too-strong coffee, all of which is why I like it, and why I eat there whenever it is open.

I was sitting in a booth at the back. I did not see her come in, or maybe she was there when I came in, but anyway I did not see her until she came out of the bathroom behind me and passed my booth or rather stopped at my booth. Now that I think about it, I did not see her until she stopped at my booth, and because I heard the restroom door slap shut I assumed that's where she came from and now that I think about it, she might have been in the restroom the whole time. To be perfectly clear, I looked up from my coffee and the wreckage of eggs and soggy wheat toast (I should have ordered white) and she was standing beside the table, puffy-faced and dirty. Her nails were cracked and bleeding. She was wearing sunglasses. She never took them off. Her arms were bruised and red—I know those bruises. I know that red.

"Talk," I heard a woman's voice say, not hers.

"They always return me to that bathroom," the UFO Girl said, somewhat clairvoyantly, I thought.

"It's not clairvoyance," she said. "All things being equal, and all."

"Talk," said the voice, not hers.

"Are all things equal?" I asked. I don't know why I was being so rude, why I didn't just ask her to sit down.

"None of this is real," she whispered.

"Oh," I said. "What a relief."

"You'd think so, wouldn't you?" she said. Need I add, sadly?

("Talk.")

"So," I said. She just stood there.

("Talk.")

"So long time no see," I said, stupidly.

"Longer than you know," she said.

"Right," I said.

"So anyway," she said. "I'll see you soon."

("Talk.")

"Do you want to sit down?" I said. I was suddenly desperately lonely.

"I'll see you soon," she said, and walked back into the bathroom.

I thought about going back and peeking in, but I just couldn't bring myself to do it. I put three dollars next to my plate and stood up and did not speak to anybody did not look at anybody did not listen to anybody did not hear anybody until I was back here.

And now back in my motel room, I have begun to be afraid. I think of the obvious ambiguity of the UFO Girl's last words. I think that it's too neat that she would be back now, here at the end, just pages from the Epilogue that I, superstitiously, wrote days ago (because now who knows where the end will be? Who knows?). Yet I am the opposite of eased. I worry that she will be back with the other abductees, that they will kick the door in, flood the room with white light. I know this is paranoia. Some sort of paranoia. I wish my Muse had not left. She will kick in the door and then they will all drift in, all of them unhappy and damaged and dirty, holding hands with little gray aliens with big heads and big dark eyes. And one little alien just for me, all alone, lifting a hand to me, pulling me to my feet, its dark eyes huge and hypnotic and black, very lonely, all of us all alone here at the end for the last terrible trick, you too, sweet sweet reader, I'm sorry about that, but you too, all of us here and alone for the great disappearing

Why did she go to see him? What was she doing at the Moon Winx Motel the day she discovered his day-old corpse?

I'm writing this now by the ocean on a breezy fall day. It's morning; the room is full of light. This is South Carolina; the breezes are still warm. Downstairs, I hear Penelope cooking breakfast, and Chloe and Miranda, Gus's daughters, singing along with old songs on the jukebox I bought them last month: "It rained all night, the day I left, the weather it was dry...."

Andrew Jr, just two months old, is sleeping in a carrier at my feet.

Why did she go back there?

After Gus's death, Penelope and I in our grief grew closer. Feelings we'd always left unspoken we felt free to speak. We have been married for a year. I tell you this so you know there was nothing unseemly in my courtship, nothing improper in our marriage. We never would have dreamed of doing anything while Penelope was married, of course. Ask anyone. Everyone looks at us and smiles, understands. We have brought joy to each other.

In death, Gus has brought a joy that he did not in life.

In the end, I don't care what she was doing at his motel. We've never discussed it. It's not important. What is important is where we are now. I look out at the ocean, feel the warm breezes stirring in the corners, hear Andrew, Jr stirring at my feet.

"When the sun came out, I froze to death…."

The only important thing is that she found this book, that she then called me. In a way, Gus is here with me still, with us all, and if you listen hard, you can hear him pulling the trigger, hear the snap:

Write as if it matters.

Live as if it matters.

— Andrew Shay